W9-BQR-978

THE ISLAND OF IMPERFECTION
PUZZLE BOOK

the text of this book is printed
on 100% recycled paper

THE ISLAND OF IMPERFECTION

PUZZLE BOOK

with Other Assorted Brainteasers

E. R. Emmet

BARNES & NOBLE BOOKS
A DIVISION OF HARPER & ROW, PUBLISHERS
New York, Cambridge, Hagerstown,
Philadelphia, San Francisco, London,
Mexico City, São Paulo, Sydney

Published simultaneously in Great Britain by Harper & Row Limited, 28 Tavistock Street, London WC2E 7PN and in Australia and New Zealand by Harper & Row (Australasia) Pty. Limited, P.O. Box 226, Artarmon, New South Wales, 2064.

FIRST EDITION
ISBN: 0-06-463512-0 (U.S.A. and Canada)
0-06-337011-5 (except U.S.A. and Canada)

80 81 82 83 84 10 9 8 7 6 5 4 3 2 1

In memory of my late wife,
who helped me more than she ever knew

Contents

(The asterisks indicate how hard the puzzle is, with 5 asterisks for the hardest ones.)

Part V   Soccer on the Island of Imperfection

Part VI   The Jokers (4 Tribes on the Island)

Part VII   Letters for Digits: Division, Addition, Multiplication

Part VIII Cross-Number Puzzles

Part IX Our Factory

Part X Soccer: Letters for Digits

Preface

The great thing about the Island of Imperfection is that almost anything can happen there, and the last 2 years have shown great changes in this wonderful Island. Many of them have been for the better, some of them I fear for the worse.

Many readers will know about the mysterious new tribe, the Jokers, which seems to have evolved from nowhere. But that is just a salutary reminder to us all of the power of nature.

In the old days there were just three tribes on the Island: the Pukkas, who always told the truth; the Wotta-Woppas, who never told the truth; and the Shilli-Shallas, who made statements that were alternately true and false or false and true. You knew where you were then, and everything was nicely cut and dried. And then the Jokers appeared. The customs and traditions that had evolved for centuries on the Island had now a new look, and in my opinion it was not a good one. Uncertainty had reared its ugly head.

But I must admit that some changes on the Island had definitely been for the better. In the past they sometimes played a certain amount of soccer, but now, I am delighted to say, that game has come to the Island in a very big way. You will find now not only the old-fashioned type of soccer puzzle but also a new kind of puzzle (new for the Island, at any rate), in which letters have been substituted for digits. Although it has not been possible to keep the Jokers altogether out of this, I am glad to say that they do not appear very often.

The number of visitors to the Island has increased considerably. Not only have there been those who told them more about soccer, but also those who taught them to read (number 33). Our Factory has paid them another visit, and no doubt more and more tourists and more and more factories will be coming soon.

I write now not as the fictitious "I" of the Island of Imperfection but as the author of this book. Apart from what has been happening on the Island, there are quite a few soccer puzzles of various kinds, and letters for digits being applied to division, addition, and multiplication.

I have been making up a large number of these puzzles for a very long time. But it is only fairly recently that I have realized how important they can be in improving the thinking power of people of all ages, perhaps especially of the young. The minds of the young (or most of them) are very active, but obviously they cannot have a great deal of knowledge, which can only come from experience and to some extent from doing a great deal of learning by rote. The great thing about puzzles is that after a bit of explanation the young can be very quick to understand what is happening, and the whole operation is likely to be enjoyed. Two important results then follow. The first is that these problems can be a pretty good test of intelligence, and the second is—and this is even more important—that doing these puzzles and enjoying them will be likely to make the mind more active and more powerful in a way that learning things by rote is less likely to do.

I am grateful to the *New Scientist,* the London *Sunday Times,* the *Retail Digest,* the *Surgical News,* and the *National Westminster Bank* magazine for allowing me to reproduce puzzles that they have already published. I hope I have become better over the years in checking my own puzzles, but it is always very important to have other people who will look at them with new eyes. Alan Summers and Simon Taylor-Young have been through every puzzle in the book and made many valuable suggestions, and many laymen have also helped. The Winchester Copying Centre and Joan H. Preston have between them typed all the puzzles in the book, and I am most grateful to them.

But above all I am grateful to my late wife. She encouraged me in general and was always on the lookout for new ideas. My reaction was sometimes to say that this was quite impossible, but a certain amount of thinking often showed what a creative instinct she had for puzzles—as for so many other things. She got great satisfaction from doing my new puzzles, usually correctly and more and more swiftly.

PART I

Starters

(1–3)

1. Furiouser and Curiouser (*)

Uncle Bungle gets things wrong. He fills us all with gloom.
Ask him just to sing a song. It will not be in tune.
Ask him to add or multiply, divide or just subtract,
Suggest that he should make a speech, wrong will be every fact.
Of all the maddening men I know, my Uncle takes the cake.
There's nothing that he will do right, no mistakes that he won't make.
But *yet*—I wonder sometimes, puzzled is what I am;
For when I looked just yesterday at a little addition sum,
I found that all the figures were incorrect by one.
Just one.
I was furious,
But also rather curious.
Here is the sum,
For you
To do:

$$
\begin{array}{r}
2\ 8\ 2\ 8 \\
3\ 2\ 2\ 7 \\
\hline
9\ 3\ 8\ 2 \\
\hline
\end{array}
$$

All figures are 1 out. Find the correct addition sum.

2. Charm or Logic? (**)

Some girls go for charm, but not Agnes. She happens to think that logic is rather more important.

It was not surprising, therefore, that she arranged a logic test for herself and five friends who were equally minded—or more or less so, anyway!

The names of her friends were Beatrice, Clarissa, Dolly, Erica, and Fanny, and I am able to give you the following details of their places in the test (there were no ties).

Dolly was one place higher than Agnes.
Beatrice was not first or last.
Erica was two places higher than Clarissa.
Fanny's place was even, and Agnes's place was odd.

What were their places in the test?

3. "All Wrong, All Wrong" (***)

A couple of 1's, a couple of 2's, and a 6;
    All wrong, all wrong!
If only I thought that the puzzle was one I could fix,
    I'd sing a song.
But as I feel sure that it's rather too much for me,
    My voice is muted.
Uncle Bungle's my name and I fear that you must agree,
    I'm rather stupid.
So please, I implore,
Continue the fight,
With tooth and with claw,
With main and with might,
To make wrong sums right.

```
                    1 - -
        2 - ) - - - - -
              6 -
              ___
              1 - -
              2 - -
              _____

                - -
                - -
                ===
```

The figures given are all incorrect. Write out the whole division problem.

PART II

Soccer

(4–7)

4. 3 Teams (*)

Some three soccer teams—A, B, and C—are to play each other
once. After some, or perhaps all, of the matches had been played,
a table giving some details of the number of matches played, won,
lost, and so on looked like this:

Team	Played	Won	Lost	Drawn	Goals for	Goals against	Points
A					3		1
B					1	5	2
C							

(2 points for a win; 1 point to each side in a drawn match)

Find the score in each match.

5. Soccer on the Island of Near Perfection (**)

On the Island of Near Perfection they always try to move with the
times. It has become increasingly obvious recently that what
people really like when they go to watch a soccer match is to see a
lot of goals scored. The Islanders have therefore made the goals
much larger and increased the time of play. The result in a recent
competition between 3 teams who are eventually going to play
each other once—or perhaps they have already done so—was as
follows:

Team	Played	Won	Lost	Drawn	Goals for	Goals against	Points
A				1	58	46	
B					40	50	1
C					34	36	

(2 points for a win; 1 for a draw)

Find the score in each match.

9

6. Uncle Bungle and the Use of Reason (**)

Four soccer teams—A, B, C, and D—are all to play each other once.

After some of the matches have been played, Uncle Bungle produces a tattered piece of paper containing some details of matches played, won, lost, drawn, and so on.

"From this," he said, "and the use of reason, it is possible to discover all the details of the matches played."

The piece of paper was like this:

Team	Played	Won	Lost	Drawn	Goals for	Goals against
A						
B			0	0	4	3
C	2				6	3
D			1	0	0	1

The reader will be surprised to hear that for once Uncle Bungle was right. It *is* possible to discover all the details of the matches played.

Can you?

7. Nearly Right (****)

Uncle Bungle does not seem to be giving away much information in his latest soccer puzzle, in which 4 teams—A, B, C, and D—were eventually going to play each other once. I am sorry about this, and I fear that you will find the situation even worse when I tell you that *one* of the figures given was wrong.

"Well anyway," he said rather proudly, "it is nearly right."

The document that he handed over to me looked like this:

Team	Played	Won	Lost	Drawn	Goals for	Goals against	Points
A	2				4	0	2
B							3
C	2		1		3	3	
D	3				8	5	2

(2 points for a win; 1 for a draw)

Which figure was incorrect? What should it be? Find the score in each match.

PART III

Division
(Some Missing Figures)
(8–9)

8. 5 Digits Divided by 2 Digits (**)

The following division sum with most of the figures missing comes out exactly:

```
          _ _ _ _
    _ _ ) _ _ _ _ _
          _ _
          _ _ 2
          _ _
          ‾‾‾‾‾
            _ _ _
            _ _ _
            ‾‾‾‾‾
```

Find the correct figures.

9. 4 Digits Divided by 2 Digits (***)

The following division sum with most of the figures missing comes out exactly

```
          _ _ _
    _ _ ) 6 _ _ _
          _ _
          ‾‾‾
          _ _ _
          _ _ 3
          ‾‾‾‾‾
            _ _
            _ 4
            ‾‾‾
```

Find the correct figures.

PART IV

The Island of Imperfection: Assorted (3 Tribes)

(10–20)

10. 1 of Each (*)

On the Island of Imperfection there are 3 tribes: the Pukkas, who always tell the truth; the Wotta-Woppas, who never tell the truth; and the Shilli-Shallas, who make statements that are alternately true and false or false and true.

Alf, Bert, and Charlie, with whom this story deals, all belong to different tribes.

They speak as follows:

ALF: Bert is a Shilli-Shalla.
BERT: Charlie is not a Shilli-Shalla.
CHARLIE: Alf's remark is true.

Find the tribes to which Alf, Bert, and Charlie belong.

11. Silly, Silent C? (*)

It really was rather maddening when C refused to make a statement.

But I had better explain. We are on the Island of Imperfection, where those who know it well are aware that there used to be three tribes. They are the Pukkas, who always tell the truth; the Wotta-Woppas, who never tell the truth; and the Shilli-Shallas, who make statements that are alternately true and false or false and true.

A, B, and C, the three inhabitants of the Island with whom we are concerned, belong to different tribes, and we are very much interested to find out which belongs to which. But C remains silent, and at first glance that does not seem to help much.

A and B speak as follows:

A: I belong to a less truthful tribe than B does.
B: I am a Shilli-Shalla.

C, as we have said, remained silent, but was he in fact being all that silly?

Find, if you can, the tribes to which A, B, and C belong.

19

12. The Door Men Come to the Island (*)

I am the managing director of Our Factory, and I write now from the wonderful Island of Imperfection.

I had better start by explaining about Our Factory. I ought really to say "My Factory," for I am the Managing Director. Over the years the personnel has doubled, and although I do not like to boast, I must say I am rather proud of that. To start off, there were only 4 people employed at the factory; now there are 8. I thought it would make a nice holiday for them if I took some of them to the Island of Imperfection.

At the time this story takes place, there are 3 tribes on the Island: the Pukkas, who always tell the truth; the Wotta-Woppas, who never tell the truth; and the Shilli-Shallas, who make statements that are alternately true and false or false and true.

The 3 members of Our Factory with which this story deals were the Door-Opener, the Door-Shutter, and the Door-Knob-Polisher. As is the custom of the Island, they were all made members of one of the 3 tribes—in fact, each one was made a member of a different tribe.

They were pretty quick to understand how the tribes worked, and I am glad to say they made no mistake in this puzzle.

I call them A, B, and C in no particular order; they spoke as follows:

A: 1. B is not a Shilli-Shalla.
    2. C is the Door-Knob-Polisher.
B: 1. C is a Pukka.
    2. A is the Door-Opener.
C: 1. A is a Wotta-Woppa.
    2. I am a Shilli-Shalla.

Find the tribes and the jobs of A, B, and C.

13. The Bumbling B (**)

On the Island of Imperfection there are 3 tribes: the Pukkas, who always tell the truth; the Wotta-Woppas, who never tell the truth; and the Shilli-Shallas, who make statements that are alternately true and false or false and true.

This story deals with 3 inhabitants of the Island, 1 from each tribe, whom we shall call A, B, and C. A and C each make a statement, but B, who goes through life in a bumbling and idle sort of way, does not in fact say anything on this occasion, although of course when he does speak he conforms to the strict rules of his tribe.

A and C's statements are as follows:

A: B is not a Wotta-Woppa.
C: If I were to ask B what tribe A belonged to, he would, quite rightly, say Shilli-Shalla.

To which tribe do A, B, and C belong?

14. Imperfect Birthdays (**)

On the Island of Imperfection there are three tribes: the Puk-kas, who always tell the truth; the Wotta-Woppas, who never tell the truth; and the Shilli-Shallas, who make statements that are alternately true and false or false and true.

This story is about four inhabitants of the Island, all of whom were born on different days in April. It is known that at least one of them was a Pukka, but no other information is obtainable about their tribes.

They speak as follows:

A: 1. All our birthdays are on even days of the month.
    2. B's third statement is true.
    3. B's birthday is earlier in the month than those of the other 3.

B: 1. D is a Pukka.
    2. None of our birthdays is on a day that is a multiple of 3.
    3. One of our birthdays is on the last day of the month.

C: 1. All our birthdays are on days that are multiples of 3.
    2. A belongs to a more truthful tribe than D does.
    3. The date of my birthday is twice the date of D's.

D: 1. A is a Wotta-Woppa.
    2. All our birthdays are on odd days of the month.
    3. My birthday is on the 11th day of the month.

Find the tribes to which A, B, C, and D belong, and the dates of their birthdays.

15. How Many of Each? (**)

It has become the custom on the Island for there to be one representative of each tribe in the talks and discussions that they have with each other. Perhaps the Islanders think that to do it like this produces a more interesting argument, especially if they are not wearing their tribal badges. This story shows that this need not be so and that there is a lot to be said for trying to find out how many there are of each tribe.

There were at the time in which this story takes place 3 tribes on the Island: the Pukkas, who always tell the truth; the Wotta-Woppas, who never tell the truth; and the Shilli-Shallas, who make statements that are alternately true and false or false and true.

This story deals with 3 natives, but it is for the reader to discover how many there are from each tribe.

They make statements as follows:

A: 1. We all belong to the same tribe.
    2. C is not a Wotta-Woppa.
B: 1. A is older than I am.
    2. A never tells the truth.
C: 1. B is a Pukka.
    2. I am a Pukka.

Is A older than B? Find the tribes to which A, B, and C belong.

16. Wine Comes to the Island (**)

It is important that those who live on our wonderful Island should become accustomed to the good things of life. Or at any rate *I* think it is important! A representative of a famous wine firm has recently paid a visit to the Island, and I am glad to say that he had some success in awakening the interest of the inhabitants.

But I had better explain. At the time of this story there were 3 tribes on the Island: the Pukkas, who always tell the truth; the Wotta-Woppas, who never tell the truth; and the Shilli-Shallas, who make statements that are alternately true and false or false and true. All those who come to the Island are forced to join one of the tribes, and the wine man was no exception. But whether he joined the tribe of his choice is hard to say.

The 4 men with whom this story deals are 3 natives, 1 from each tribe, and the representative of the famous wine firm. We shall call them A, B, C, and D in no particular order.

Clearly the wine man wants to sell a few bottles, and he succeeds in selling 1 to the representative of one tribe, 2 to the representative of another, and 3 to the representative of the third.

They make statements as follows:

A: 1. B is not a Wotta-Woppa.
   2. The wine man is a Pukka.
B: 1. I am the wine man.
   2. D is a Pukka.
C: 1. I purchased 2 bottles.
   2. A is a Wotta-Woppa.
D: 1. There are 2 Wotta-Woppas among us.
   2. I purchased 3 bottles.

Who is the wine man? Find the tribes to which they all belong and how many bottles each native purchased.

17. A Wink and a Nod (***)

We live, we 3, on the Imperfect Isle,
Where all is not just what it ought to be.
One is a Wotta-Woppa, and he never
Tells what is true, in fact a liar he.
And then there is another one who cannot
Make up his mind. Oh, shall I tell a lie?
He is a Shilli-Shalla, and makes statements,
One true, one false. But which? The constant cry.
The third one is a Pukka, and we find
Nothing but truth comes from the third man's mind.
Single figures all our dwellings,
And each one is different.
Three statements each, so read with care
And use your loaf to find what's meant.

A: 1. First let me say no Shilli-Shalla I,
But I'm afraid I cannot tell you why!
2. Then I point out that where numbers are concerned
The lower the truer; that's the fact for which you
yearned.
3. Thirdly, no tricks,
My number's less than 6.

B: 1 and 2. A Pukka, I, and live at No. 1.
That's two statements in a single line.
3. Perfect, you might say, but not as perfect as
The square that is C's number.

C: 1. A and B live on either side of me.
2. Who is the Wotta-Woppa? Why, it's B.
3. And now our verse
Has done its worst.
Just to finish with a wink,
To get this right you'll have to think.
And with a nod,
A's number is not odd.

Where do A, B, and C live and what are their tribes?

18. Some Old Men on the Island (***)

There are 3 tribes on the Island of Imperfection: the Pukkas, who always tell the truth; the Wotta-Woppas, who never tell the truth; and the Shilli-Shallas, who make statements that are alternately true and false or false and true.

This story deals with 4 men whom we shall call A, B, C, and D, and there is at least 1 representative of each tribe among them.

They make statements in accordance with their tribal characteristics as follows:

A: 1. My age is a multiple of 6.
        2. My age is not the same as B's age.
        3. D belongs to a more truthful tribe than I do.

B: 1. I am older than A.
        2. The ages of A and C are the same.
        3. D's age is a multiple of 12.

C: 1. I am older than A.
        2. D's age is even.
        3. B's second remark is true.

D: 1. B is 3 times as old as C.
        2. My age is 12 more than A's age.
        3. C's age is a multiple of 13.

People tend to live for a long time on this wonderful Island, but none of the 4 with whom this story deals is older than 105.

Find the tribes to which each man belongs and the age of each man.

19. On the Silly Side of Silly Street (****)

On the Island of Imperfection there are 3 tribes: the Pukkas, who always tell the truth; the Wotta-Woppas, who never tell the truth; and the Shilli-Shallas, who make statements that are alternately true and false or false and true.

The 4 inhabitants of the Island with whom this story deals live in separate houses all on one side of Silly Street, where the numbers of the houses are all odd, from 1 to 41 inclusive.

They speak as follows:

A: 1. D's number is one-third of C's.
    2. D is a Wotta-Woppa.

B: 1. The numbers of all our 4 houses are multiples of 5.
    2. C's number is less than A's.

C: 1. A belongs to the same tribe as I do.
    2. A Pukka lives in No. 35.

D: 1. C's number is greater than B's.
    2. B belongs to a more truthful tribe than I do.

You are told that there is at least one representative from each tribe but only one Shilli-Shalla.

Find their tribes and the numbers of their houses.

20. The Poorer the Truer (*****)

There are 3 tribes on the Island of Imperfection: the Pukkas, who always tell the truth; the Wotta-Woppas, who never tell the truth; and the Shilli-Shallas, who make statements that are alternately true and false or false and true.

It is sad to record that recently the inhabitants of the Island have become interested in material gain, and therefore even less perfect. The Golden Age, in fact, has been replaced by the golden wage.

The 4 in this story (we shall call them A, B, C, and D) are all earning wages that are not less than 15 hopes and not more than 30 hopes a week. (A hope is a unit of the currency on the Island.)

In every case their weekly earnings are an exact number of hopes. One of them is a Pukka, one is a Wotta-Woppa, and the other 2 are Shilli-Shallas. Their wages are all different, and it happens that their truthfulness in the 3 remarks recorded below ascends as their wages descend. But whether this is cause and effect or coincidence we shall probably never know. Three of the 4 are married; we shall call their wives X, Y, and Z in no particular order.

They make remarks as follows:

A: 1. The Wotta-Woppas wages are 20 percent greater than those of one of the Shilli-Shallas.
2. The difference between my wages and B's is 10 hopes a week.
3. D's weekly wages are a multiple of 4 hopes.

B: 1. Z's husband's weekly wages are an even number of hopes.
2. I am a Shilli-Shalla.
3. The best paid of us is married to X.

C: 1. One of the Shilli-Shallas earns 33⅓ percent more than the Pukka.
2. The Pukka is a bachelor.
3. B's wages are less than mine.

D: 1. The weekly wages of one of us is a prime number of hopes.

2. The difference between the weekly wages of the two Shilli-Shallas is 1 hope.
3. One of the Shilli-Shallas is married to Z.

Find to which tribe each man belongs, his weekly wages, and to whom, if anyone, he is married.

PART V

Soccer on the Island of Imperfection

(21–25)

21. What the Secretaries Said (***)

There has been a great craze for soccer recently on the Island of Imperfection, and I have been fortunate enough to get some details of games played there.

There are 3 tribes on the Island: the Pukkas, who always tell the truth; the Wotta-Woppas, who never tell the truth; and the Shilli-Shallas, who make statements that are alternately true and false or false and true.

Three teams, 1 from each tribe, have been having a competition, in which eventually they will all play each other—or perhaps they have already done this. The secretaries of the 3 teams have been asked to give details of the number of matches played, won, lost, and so on, and of course they do this in accordance with the rules of their tribes—so that, for example, all the figures given by the secretary of the Wotta-Woppa team will be wrong.

The figures given are as follows (calling the teams A, B, and C in no particular order):

Team	Played	Won	Lost	Drawn	Goals for	Goals against
A	2	1	0	1	3	2
B	1	2	2	0	4	3
C	2	2	2	1	0	2

(In no case did a team win by a majority of more than 3 goals.)

Find the tribe to which each of the 3 teams belongs and the score in each match.

22. Soccer Makes Us Less Imperfect (***)

In recent years we have been having more and more contact with the outside world, so it is not surprising that what is I suppose the world's most popular game has been accepted with alacrity on the Island and perhaps has helped a little in making the life there rather less imperfect.

But I had better explain. At the time of this story there are three tribes on the Island: the Pukkas, who always tell the truth; the Wotta-Woppas, who never tell the truth; and the Shilli-Shallas, who make statements that are alternately true and false or false and true.

Three teams, one from each tribe, are eventually going to play each other once—or perhaps they have already done so. Details of the number of matches played, won, lost, and so on are given below, but not unnaturally the secretaries of the three teams gave the details about the matches according to their tribal rules—so that, for example, only the figures given by the Pukkas's secretary will be entirely correct.

The figures given are as follows (calling the teams A, B, and C in no particular order):

Team	Played	Won	Lost	Drawn	Goals for	Goals against	Points
A	1	0	2	1	2	5	3
B	2	1	0	1	4	1	3
C	2	1	1	0	0	2	1

(2 points for a win; 1 to each side in a drawn match. In no case did a team win by a margin of more than 3 goals.)

Find the tribe to which each of the three teams belongs and the score in each match.

23. We Try Letters for Digits (**)

No one could say that the inhabitants of the Island of Imperfection are slow in coming forward. Somehow or other the news has come through that there is a new kind of soccer puzzle, and naturally they want to try it.

There are 3 tribes on the Island: the Pukkas, who always tell the truth; the Wotta-Woppas, who never tell the truth; and the Shilli-Shallas, who make statements that are alternately true and false or false and true. This story deals with a soccer team from each tribe, whom we shall call A, B, and C in no particular order.

The letters below stand for digits (from 0 to 9), and each letter stands for a different digit. If A, for example, was a Pukka, then reading across all his letters would be correct, and if B was a Shilli-Shalla his letters reading across would be alternately true and false or false and true, and if C was a Wotta-Woppa all his letters would be incorrect.

The teams are eventually going to play each other once—or perhaps they have already done so.

The table that you are given is as follows:

Team	Played	Won	Lost	Drawn	Goals for	Goals against	Points
A	m	y	k	d	x	y	x
B	m	x	x	y	m	m	m
C	x	d	x	x	y	m	y

Find the score in each match.

24. Uncle Bungle Gets Things Right (***)

The game of soccer has been becoming more and more popular on the Island, and somebody—(who can it be?)—has been making up puzzles about this wonderful game with letters substituted for digits.

But some explanation is needed. At the time of this story there are 3 tribes on the Island: the Pukkas, who always tell the truth; the Wotta-Woppas, who never tell the truth; and the Shilli-Shallas, who make statements that are alternately true and false or false and true.

If the B team, for example, are Pukkas, then all the letters will be correct; if the B team are Shilli-Shallas, the letters will be alternately true and false or false and true; and if they are Wotta-Woppas, the letters will all be false.

As a matter of fact, when I said, "Who can it be?" I had a sneaking suspicion that it was Uncle Bungle, who had been paying a visit to the Island. And I was right. But just for once Uncle made no mistakes.

The table that was produced by the representative of each tribe was as follows:

Team	Played	Won	Lost	Drawn	Goals for	Goals against	Points
A	g	h	k	k	k	h	g
B	k	y	t	g	g	p	h
C	g	k	h	k	p	h	p

Find the score in each match.

25. A Couple of Pukkas (****)

People and teams on the Island of Imperfection often seem to go about in 3's, 1 from each tribe. But things do not have to happen like that, and in the latest soccer puzzles I offer my readers, in which 4 teams were concerned, there were 2 Pukka soccer teams but only 1 Wotta-Woppa team and 1 Shilli-Shalla team.

But I had better explain. There were at the time of this story 3 tribes on the Island: the Pukkas, who always tell the truth; the Wotta-Woppas, who never tell the truth; and the Shilli-Shillas, who make statements that are alternately true and false or false and true. If, for example, A is a Wotta-Woppa, A's games played, won, lost, and so on will all be incorrect. The situation has been made more interesting by the fact that letters have been substituted for digits. Each letter stands for a digit from 0 to 9.

A, B, C, and D are all eventually going to play each other once—or perhaps they have already done so.

The details, which the reader is no doubt longing to see, are as follows:

Team	Played	Won	Lost	Drawn	Goals for	Goals against	Points
A	m	m	g	t	t	y	m
B	m	g	m	g	g	k	g
C	t	p	g	m	x	t	k
D	t	t	y	m	p	k	p

(2 points for a win; 1 to each side in a drawn match)

Find the score in each match.

PART VI

The Jokers (4 Tribes on the Island)

(26–35)

26. C Is Silent (*)

Four tribes seem now, for better or worse, to be firmly established on the Island of Imperfection. They are the Pukkas, who always tell the truth; the Wotta-Woppas, who never tell the truth; the Shilli-Shallas, who make statements that are alternately true and false or false and true; and the Jokers, whose rules for truth-telling in making 3 statements are any rules that are different from those of any of the other 3 tribes.

In the story I have to tell about A, B, C, and D, there is 1 member of each tribe. C, I am afraid, does not actually say anything. Can he just be fed up? I don't blame him.

The other three speak as follows:

A: 1. B is a Pukka.
B: 1. C is a Shilli-Shalla.
D: 1. A is a Pukka.
    2. I am a Shilli-Shalla or a Wotta-Woppa.
    3. B is a Joker.

Find the tribes to which A, B, C, and D belong.

27. All Four of Us Are Here (*)

Some people may find it nice to have a simple puzzle with 1 representative of each of the 4 tribes. One then knows a bit more where one is and what is happening.

On the Island of Imperfection there are now 4 tribes: the Pukkas, who always tell the truth; the Wotta-Woppas, who never tell the truth; the Shilli-Shallas, who make statements that are alternately true and false or false and true; and a fourth tribe, which has recently added itself somehow to the Island and which is called the Jokers. All I am prepared to tell you about the Jokers' truth-telling is that in making 3 statements their rules are any rules that are different from those of the other 3 tribes. We will call our characters A, B, C, and D in no particular order.

They make statements as follows:

A: 1. D is not a Pukka.
   2. C belongs to a more truthful tribe than D does.
B: 1. Either A or D is a Pukka.
   2. I am not a Joker.
   3. A is a Wotta-Woppa.
C: 1. A never tells the truth.
D: 1. B is a Wotta-Woppa.

Find the tribes to which A, B, C, and D belong.

28. A Was Absent (**)

Things have got very slack on the Island recently, since the arrival of the Jokers, and I am afraid it seems to happen quite often now that when people are really needed they are not to be found. The other day, for example, in one of the tribal tests—which are, and I hope always will be, an integral part of life in this wonderful place—A was just not to be found. But I had better explain.

There are 4 tribes on the island. The Pukkas, who always tell the truth; the Wotta-Woppas, who never tell the truth; the Shilli-Shallas, who make statements that are alternately true and false or false and true; and the Jokers, whose rules when 3 statements are made are any rules that are different from those of the other 3 tribes.

This story deals with 4 men—A, B, C, and D—one from each tribe.

B, C, and D speak as follows:

B: 1. I am a Joker.
    2. C sometimes tells the truth.
    3. D is a Pukka.
C: 1. A is a Pukka.
D: 1. B is a Joker.

But where was A? Although he was not around, you should be able to find the tribes to which the 4 men belong.

29. The Jokers Play Soccer (**)

As my readers will know, I am very keen on soccer, and they will also know that I am far from being keen on the Jokers—the new tribe that in some mysterious way has recently appeared on the Island of Imperfection. Just think of my distress, then, when these 2 things were put together and the Jokers started playing soccer. But an explanation is badly needed.

There used to be 3 tribes on the Island: the Pukkas, who always tell the truth; the Wotta-Woppas, who never tell the truth; and the Shilli-Shallas, who make statements that are alternately true and false or false and true. The Jokers are a new and different and in my opinion a very unsatisfactory tribe. All I can tell you about their truth-telling rules is that in making 3 statements they use any rules that are different from those of any of the other 3 tribes. This puzzle is about 4 teams—A, B, C, and D—1 from each tribe.

I am a great one for rules, as my readers will know, and I am glad to say that there are some here. You are told, for instance, that each match that was won was won by 1 goal and at least 1 goal was scored in every match. I also approve of the fact that in this puzzle the score in each match was different and that the digits that are wrong are wrong by 1. It so happens that the Shilli-Shalla captain, who sometimes finds it difficult to remember whether he is coming or going, starts what he has to say here with a true statement.

The 4 captains all make 3 statements. For example, A's first statement is that they lost 2 matches, A's second statement is that they had 1 goal for, and his third statement is that they had no goals against.

The table that I can give you is as follows:

Team	Played	Won	Lost	Drawn	Goals for	Goals against	Points
A			2		1	0	
B	1			2			0
C	3				4	2	
D	1			1			0

(2 points for a win; 1 to each side in a drawn match)

Find the tribes to which A, B, C, and D belong and the score in each match.

30. C Was Far from Silent (**)

There are some things that one must learn to live with, however much one disapproves. And that is what I was beginning to feel about the fourth tribe on the Island of Imperfection.

There used to be 3 tribes on the Island: the Pukkas, who always told the truth; the Wotta-Woppas, who never told the truth; and the Shilli-Shallas, who made statements that were alternately true and false or false and true. But a fourth tribe has now been added, and they call themselves the Jokers. And all that one can say about this tribe is that in making 3 statements their truth-telling rules are any rules that are different from those of the other 3 tribes.

A, B, C, and D are 4 inhabitants of the Island, 1 from each tribe.

They make statements as follows:

A: 1. C is not a Wotta-Woppa.
B: 1. I am a Joker.
C: 1. B is a Pukka.
    2. B sometimes tells the truth.
    3. I am a Pukka.
D: 1. C makes three true statements.

Find the tribes to which A, B, C, and D belong.

31. Our Factory on the Island (***)

I had heard some time ago about the fabulous Island of Imperfection, and I longed to go there. I must say it sounded pretty perfect to me; for example, if one belonged to one of the tribes one knew where one was and had clear principles to follow. And what could be more perfect than that?

But I had better explain. I am the managing director of a factory. Some people might say that it was rather an old-fashioned one, as might perhaps be seen from the jobs of the 4 men (Alf, Bert, Charlie, and Duggie) whom I was going to take with me. These jobs, of course, change from time to time, but their last jobs had been, in no particular order, those of Sweeper-Upper, Door-Opener, Door-Shutter, and Worker.

The Island of Imperfection is not so easy to explain. There are now 4 tribes on this island: the Pukkas, who always tell the truth; the Wotta-Woppas, who never tell the truth; the Shilli-Shallas, who make statements that are true and false or false and true; and a fourth tribe, the Jokers, which has recently been added or has evolved (how wonderful nature is). All I can tell you about the truth-telling rules of the Jokers is that in making 3 statements their rules are different from those of any of the other 3 tribes.

When we arrived on the Island, it was natural for Alf, Bert, Charlie, and Duggie to join one of the 4 tribes, each a different one, and they each made 3 statements. (I thought it was very clever of them to do this very quickly without making any mistakes, but mistakes there were none.)

ALF: 1. I am the Worker.
2. Duggie makes more true statements in this puzzle than I do.
3. The Pukka is the Door-Opener.

BERT: 1. Charlie is a Wotta-Woppa.
2. Alf is the Worker.
3. Duggie is a Joker.

CHARLIE: 1. Alf is not a Pukka.
2. I am the Worker.
3. The Shilli-Shalla is the Sweeper-Upper.

DUGGIE: 1. Alf is a Joker.
2. The Joker's first statement is false.
3. Bert is not a Pukka.

Find Alf, Bert, Charlie, and Duggie's jobs and the tribes to which they are attached.

32. The Joke That Did Not Amuse (***)

I am sorry to say that the Jokers seem now to be firmly installed on the Island. Why can't things stay as they always used to be when I was young! But facts are facts, and we must try to deal with things as they are.

But I had better explain the situation. There used to be 3 tribes on the Island: the Pukkas, who always tell the truth; the Wotta-Woppas, who never tell the truth; and the Shilli-Shallas, who make statements that are alternately true and false or false and true. But now there is a new tribe, the Jokers, and all that one can say about this tribe is that in making 3 statements their truth-telling rules are any rules that are different from those of the other 3 tribes.

A, B, C, and D are 4 inhabitants of the island, 1 from each tribe, and from the 3 statements that each of them makes we shall try to discover which tribe they belong to and the numbers of the shacks in which they live. The shacks of one tribe are from 1 to 10 inclusive, of another tribe they are from 11 to 20 inclusive, of a third tribe they are from 21 to 30 inclusive, and the Jokers, who have not been very long on the island, live in shacks whose numbers are between 31 and 35.

They make statements as follows:

A: 1. The number of my shack is less than that of C's shack.
   2. The number of C's shack is odd.
   3. B's second remark is false.
B: 1. C is a Pukka.
   2. The number of D's shack is a multiple of the number of A's shack.
   3. C is not a Pukka.
C: 1. The number of A's shack is a multiple of 7.
   2. The number of my shack is a multiple of 3.
   3. B is a Joker.

D: 1. The number of my shack is less than the number of A's shack.
2. The number of B's shack is a multiple of 5.
3. A makes more true remarks than I do.

Find the tribes to which A, B, C, and D belong and the numbers of their shacks.

33. Reading Comes to the Island (***)

Education has recently come to the Island of Imperfection in a big way, but who or what is responsible for that I would not like to say. We have had quite a lot of interesting visitors lately, and perhaps it is all due to what they have said and suggested. Anyway, the fact is that the Islanders are now pretty good at reading, and one hopes that other things may follow.

But I had better explain. There are now 4 tribes on the Island: the Pukkas, who always tell the truth; the Wotta-Woppas, who never tell the truth; the Shilli-Shallas, who make statements that are alternately true and false or false and true; and the Jokers. All that one can say about the truth-telling rules of the Jokers is that in making 3 statements their rules are different from those of any of the other 3 tribes. This story deals with 4 Islanders, 1 from each tribe.

The Jokers have arranged to sell books on the Island in order to help this new surge in education, and each of the other 3 buys at least 1 book, but they all buy a different number. We shall call them A, B, C, and D in no particular order.

They make statements as follows:

A: 1. C is a Shilli-Shalla.
    2. D is not a Joker.
    3. Eight books were sold all together.
B: 1. C is not a Shilli-Shalla.
    2. I bought 4 books.
    3. A is not a Pukka.
C: 1. I am a Joker.
    2. D purchased 1 book.
    3. B is a Wotta-Woppa.
D: 1. B is not a Shilli-Shalla.
    2. Seven books were sold all together.
    3. At least one of B's statements is true.

Find the tribes to which A, B, C, and D belong and the number of books purchased by the 3 men who were not Jokers.

34. How Was the Joker's Logic? (***)

With advancing years, I am perhaps rather slow to accept things, and not inclined to be too worried if there is change and decay in most of the things I see. But I have now taken a big decision and recognized that the Jokers are on the Island. (Forever? Who knows?)

But I had better explain. There are now 4 tribes on the Island of Imperfection. The Pukkas, who always tell the truth; the Wotta-Woppas, who never tell the truth; the Shilli-Shallas, who make statements that are alternately true and false or false and true; and the Jokers, whose rules when they make 3 statements are any rules that are different from those of any of the other 3 tribes.

This story deals with four men—A, B, C, and D—one from each tribe. The extent to which the Joker has now been accepted may be judged from the fact that he is being allowed to take part in a logic test, which would I am sure be of very great interest to my readers, but unfortunately I am not able to disclose the details.

A, B, C, and D speak as follows:

A: 1. B is a Joker.
    2. D's second statement is false.
B: 1. One and only 1 of C's statements is true.
    2. The Wotta-Woppa was 2 places higher in the logic test than the Pukka.
C: 1. A is a Wotta-Woppa.
    2. D is a Shilli-Shalla.
D: 1. A is a Pukka.
    2. C was higher than A in the logic test.

Find the tribes to which A, B, C, and D belong and give as much information as you can about their places in the logic test.

35. Only One Joker—but What About the Other Tribes? (***)

There was a time on the Island when the inhabitants used to go around and discuss things with one another with only one member of each tribe taking part. But for whatever reason— perhaps just because of realizing the bonds that hold members of the same tribe together—they are often to be found now in groups in which all the tribes may or may not be represented.

They are now 4 tribes on the Island: the Pukkas, who always tell the truth; the Wotta-Woppas, who never tell the truth; the Shilli-Shallas, who make statements that are alternately true and false or false and true; and the Jokers. All I can tell you about the truth-telling rules of the Jokers is that in making 3 statements their rules are any rules that are different from those of the other 3 tribes.

This story deals with 4 people who are talking to one another, and we shall call them A, B, C, and D, in no particular order. The only information that I can give you about their tribes is that one of them is a Joker.

They make statements as follows: .

A: 1. D is a Joker.
    2. There is not much difference in this puzzle between the number of false statements and the number of true statements.
    3. D makes more true statements than B.
B: 1. C is a Pukka.
    2. A's second statement is not true.
    3. I am a Joker.
C: 1. No one makes more true statements than D.
    2. A is a Wotta-Woppa.
D: 1. B is a Shilli-Shalla or a Wotta-Woppa.
    2. Three of us belong to the same tribe.
    3. C is not a Pukka.

Find the tribes to which A, B, C, and D belong.

PART VII

Letters for Digits: Division, Addition, Multiplication

(36–44)

---

36. 5 Digits Divided by 2 Digits (**)

In the following division sum, each letter stands for a different digit.

Rewrite the sum with the letters replaced by digits.

```
                    x  b  k  g
          g  t ) d  s  x  d  m
                 d  x
                 ───
                    x  x  d
                    x  t  k
                    ──────
                          p  m
                          p  g
                          ────
                             h
                          ════
```

37. 4 Digits Divided by 2 Digits (***)

In the following division sum, each letter stands for a different digit:

```
                 b  g  p
       d  k ) k  x  m  k
              g  m
              ───
              d  p  m
              d  m  t
              ──────
                 t  k
                 x  b
                 ────
                 d  b
```

Rewrite the sum with the letters replaced by digits.

38. Division—but What Has Happened to the Divisor and the Answer? (****)

In making up his latest division sum, with letters substituted for digits, Uncle Bungle has this time left out not only the divisor but also the answer.

What is left looks like this:

```
)  s  s  t  r  d  m  m  v  v
   r  d
   _____
      d  t
      r  d
      _____
         v  x  r
         v  x  v
         _____
               x  d
               v  y
               _____
                  y  m
                  d  s
                  _____
                     x  m
                     v  y
                     _____
                        t  v  v
                        t  t  s
                        _____
                           s
```

Find the divisor and all the digits of the sum, including the answer.

39. I Lose My Specs (***)

In the division sum below, letters stand for different digits. But unfortunately I did not have my specs with me when I copied it out, and I discovered later that I had made a mistake. *One* letter was wrong on one of the occasions when it appeared.

```
              c  h  b  m
        _____
  i  c ) b  p  k  g  c  x
         m  h  x
        _____
            s  m  g
            s  k  p
           _____
               b  c  c
               m  b  i
              _____
                  g  x
                  i  c
                 _____
                  m  i
                 ========
```

Find the incorrect letter, and rewrite the sum with the letters replaced by digits.

40. Division: Some Letters for Digits, Some Missing (***)

In the following division sum, most of the digits are missing, but some are replaced by letters. The same letter stands for the same digit whenever it appears:

```
              – –  m  k
        – – ) – – – – – – k
              – k –
              ─────
                – m –
              k – –
              ─────
                    – –
                  – m
                  ───
                    m
                  ═══
```

Find the correct sum.

41. Addition (2 Numbers) (**)

In the following addition sum, the digits have been replaced by letters. The same letter stands for the same digit wherever it appears, and different letters stand for different digits.

```
    B  H  C  X  D  B  F
    D  M  A  C  G  B  F
  ──────────────────────
  F  B  B  G  B  M  G  B
  ══════════════════════
```

Find the digits for which the letters stand.

42. Addition (3 Numbers) (***)

Below is an addition sum with letters substituted for digits. The same letter stands for the same digit wherever it appears, and different letters stand for different digits:

```
    E R K K T
    E S E D T
    E K K T T
    ─────────
    T T R V T
```

Write the sum out with numbers substituted for digits.

43. Addition: Uncle's Error (****)

In the addition sum below, with letters substituted for digits, all is not, I fear, as it should be. Each letter ought to stand for the same digit wherever it appears, and different letters ought to stand for different digits; but Uncle Bungle has once more failed us, and there is 1 mistake (that is to say that 1 of the letters is wrong on 1 of the occasions on which it appears—if it appears more than once).

```
    B L A L E D Y
    B Y S X P S Y
    B L A X E P Y
    ─────────────
    Y Y R R S G G B
```

Find the mistake, and write out the correct addition sum.

44. Multiplication (**)

In the multiplication sum below the digits have been replaced by letters. The same letter stands for the same digit whenever it appears, and different letters stand for different digits.

```
    E  B  P  N  Y  E
                   E
   ─────────────────
    Y  N  H  Y  A  X
   ═════════════════
```

Write the sum out with letters replaced by digits.

PART VIII

Cross-Number Puzzles

(45–46)

45. Cross-Number Puzzle (3 by 3) (*)

1	2	3
4		
■	5	

(There are no 0's.)

Across

1. The digits are all even.
4. Odd, and even when reversed.
5. 19 is a factor of this.

Down

1. A perfect square.
2. A perfect square when reversed.
3. Each digit is 1 less than the one before.

46. Cross-Number Puzzle, with One Clue Wrong (5 by 5) (****)

(There are no 0's.)

One of the clues that follow is incorrect.

Across

1. Each digit is greater than the one before.
5. The same when reversed.
6. A perfect cube.
7. The sum of the digits is 5 less than 3 more than the square of an even number.
8. Digits all odd, and each one is less than the one before.
9. A prime factor of 4 down.
10. A factor of 7 across.

Down

1. Digits all different and all less than 6.
2. The sum of the digits is 27.
3. Odd.
4. A multiple of 25.
5. A multiple of 8.
7. A perfect square.
8. Even. Sum of digits is 11.

Find the incorrect clue, and the correct solution.

PART IX

Our Factory

(47–49)

47. "Our Factory Started with Just a Sweeper-Upper" (**)

Long years ago, when Alf and Bert were tougher,
Our Factory started with just a Sweeper-Upper.
But soon we found that other jobs were needed.
Doors must be opened, bottles must be washed.
Charlie joined the staff, and Duggie followed after;
An officer of welfare, and Ernie was his name,
And then came a Worker who brought the Factory fame.

"I am the Worker," said Duggie clear and loud,
"And the Sweeper-Upper's Charlie," and this was louder yet.
But although Duggie was looking rather proud,
One of his statements was false, I much regret.
Alf has not the Worker's or the Bottle-Washer's lot,
Five men there are, five jobs as well. Find out just who does what.

Who does what?

48. French and Mathematics at the Factory (**)

There has been a lot of excitement recently about an examination that 4 of our employees—Alf, Bert, Charlie, and Duggie—have taken in French and mathematics.

Now that we are in the Common Market, it is important that we should move with the times and learn some French. And in a modern factory such as ours we must know about all the latest mathematical ideas.

It is interesting that Bert's French place was as much above his mathematics place as Charlie's mathematics place was below his French place. Alf's place was even at both subjects, and Duggie's place was odd at both. Bert was not top at either subject, and no one had the same place at both. There were no ties.

Find the order in both subjects.

69

49. Rules (****)

No organization can be efficient without clear-cut rules setting out exactly the rewards and the responsibilities of those who have the honor to be members of the team.

As the managing director of Our Factory, therefore, I think it of the greatest importance that these rules should be put on the Society's notice board for all to see and understand.

At the time of this story, there are only 4 employees in the Factory—Alf, Bert, Charlie, and Duggie—and their jobs, not necessarily respectively, were those of Door-Shutter, Door-Opener, Bottle-Washer, and Worker.

The notice I put up, referring to their weekly wages, read as follows:

Rules

1. The Door-Opener is to get 10 percent less than 20 percent more than Charlie.
2. Bert is to get 25 percent more than £2 less than the Bottle-Washer.
3. The Door-Opener is to be paid £3 less than the Worker.
4. Bert is to be paid more than Alf.
5. Your wages are all to be a multiple of 10 pence; no one is to get more than £29 or less than £19.

Find the jobs and the wages of all my employees.

PART X

Soccer: Letters for Digits

(50–52)

---

50. 3 Teams (**)

Three soccer teams (A, B, and C) are to play each other once. After some of the matches had been played, a table was drawn up giving some details of the numbers won, lost, drawn, and so on.

But unfortunately, some letters have been substituted for digits (from 0 to 9). The same letter stands for the same digit wherever it appears, and different letters stand for different digits.

Team	Played	Won	Lost	Drawn	Goals for	Goals against	Points
A	t				x	p	
B	x		r		n	g	d
C	t				p	d	

(2 points for a win; 1 point to each side in a draw)

Find the score in each match.

51. 4 Teams (***)

Four soccer teams—A, B, C, and D—are to play each other once. After some of the games had been played, a table was drawn up giving some details of the matches played, won, lost, and so on.

But unfortunately, the digits had been replaced by letters. Each letter stands for the same digit (from 0 to 9) wherever it appears, and different letters stand for different digits.

The table looked like this:

Team	Played	Won	Lost	Drawn	Goals for	Goals against	Points
A	k				k	x	t
B				t	y		
C	x	s			h		g
D				k	k	k	

(2 points for a win; 1 to each side in a draw)

Find the score in each match.

52. Soccer and Addition (***)

In the following soccer table and addition sum, letters have been substituted for digits (from 0 to 9). The same letter stands for the same digit whenever it appears, and different letters stand for different digits.

The 4 teams are eventually going to play each other once—or perhaps they have already done so.

(i)

Team	Played	Won	Lost	Drawn	Goals for	Goals against	Points
A					y	g	
B	y	m	p		k	f	f
C				t	m	m	
D					p	t	p

(ii)

$$\begin{array}{r} x \\ + \; x \\ \hline h \\ \hline \end{array}$$

(2 points for a win; 1 point for a draw)

Find the scores in the soccer matches and write the addition sum out with numbers substituted for letters.

Solutions

1. Furiouser and Curiouser

Remember that in every case figures *are 1 out*. Look first at figures on the extreme right:

$$8$$
$$7$$
$$\overline{}$$
$$2$$
$$=$$

If 8 were 9 and 7 were 8, we would have: $9 + 8 = 17$ (not possible). If 8 were 9 and 7 were 6 (or if 8 were 7 and 7 were 8) we would have: $9 + 6$ (or $7 + 8$) $= 15$ (not possible). If 8 were 7 and 7 were 6, we would have: $7 + 6 = 13$—and this is the only possibility.

Consider the third line down:

2 (remember that there is 1
2 that has been carried)
—
8
=

If both 2's were 1, we would have $1 + 1 + 1 = 3$ (no). If one 2 were 1, and the other 3, then $1 + 3 + 1 = 5$ (no). If both 2's were 3, then $3 + 3 + 1 = 7$ (yes).

Consider the second line down:

8 (1 has *not* been carried from
2 third line down)
—
3
=

If 8 were 7 and 2 were 1, then $7 + 1 = 8$ (no). If 8 were 7 and 2 were 3 (or if 8 were 9 and 2 were 1), we would have $7 + 3$ (or $9 + 1$) $= 10$ (no). If 8 were 9, and 2 were 3, then $9 + 3 = 12$ (yes).

Consider the first line down:

$$
\begin{array}{r}
2 \\
3 \\
\hline
9 \\
\hline
\end{array}
\quad
\begin{array}{l}
\text{(1 has been carried from} \\
\text{second line down)}
\end{array}
$$

The 9 can only be 8. ∴ 2 and 3 must be 3 and 4, making: 3 + 4 + 1 = 8.

Complete Solution

$$
\begin{array}{r}
3\ 9\ 3\ 7 \\
4\ 3\ 3\ 6 \\
\hline
8\ 2\ 7\ 3 \\
\hline
\end{array}
$$

2. Charm or Logic?

The information that we are given can be set out as follows:

1.	D			E		A
2.	D	A	B	E		F
3.	D	A	B	E	C		A
4.	D	A	B	E	C	F
5.	D	A	B		C		A
6.		A			C	F

Both sets of information about A must be correct; ∴ A cannot be second or fourth or sixth, and since D was one place higher than A, A cannot be first. ∴ A must be third or fifth.

And since D was 1 place higher than A, D must be second or fourth.

∴ E must be first (no one else can be).

And since E was 2 places higher than C, C was third.

∴ F was sixth (no one else can be).

And since A was not third, A must be fifth; ∴ D was fourth; ∴ B was second.

Complete Solution

1. Erica
2. Beatrice
3. Clarissa
4. Dolly
5. Agnes
6. Fanny

3. "All Wrong, All Wrong"

```
                1 - -                    (i)
    2 - ) - - - -                        (ii)
            6 -                          (iii)
         ────
            1 - -                        (iv)
            2 - -                        (v)
         ────
              - -                        (vi)
              - -                        (vii)
         ════
```

From first figure in (i), (iii) must be at least 2 times the divisor. The first figure in (iv) is at least 2; ∴ (iii) starts with 7 or less (9 − 7 = 2). ∴ the divisor is 3 −, or less (but not 2 −, figure given). And since the first figure in (iv) is 2 or more, the divisor cannot be 1 − [it would not be necessary to bring down third figure in (iv)]. ∴ the divisor is 3 −. ∴ (iii) is the divisor times 2 (3 times 3 − would be too much). ∴ the first figure in (i) is 2.

And since (iii) does not start with 6, it starts with 7. ∴ the first figure in (iv) must be 2, and the first figure in (ii) must be 9. And the first figure in (v) must be 1, and (v) must be 191 or more.

And from (iii) (7 −), the divisor must be 35 or more. ∴ we want a multiple of 35, 36, 37, 38, or 39 that is between 191 and 199.

35 times 5 = 175 (no); 36 times 5 = 180 (no); 37 times 5 = 185 (no); 38 times 5 = 190 (no); but 39 times 5 = 195, and this is what we want.

∴ the divisor is 39, the second figure in (i) is 5, and (v) is 195.

(iii) is 78, and (vi) and (vii) are 78 [if they were 39, (iv) would be less than 200].

Add up from the bottom and we get:

```
              2 5 2
      3 9 ) 9 8 2 8
            7 8
            ─────
            2 0 2
            1 9 5
              ─────
              7 8
              7 8
              ═════
```

4. 3 Teams

B got 2 points, but they had 5 points against and only 1 goal for. ∴ B won 1 (1–0) and lost 1 (0–5).

A got 1 point, ∴ they drew a match. This was not vs. B, ∴ it must have been vs. C. ∴ C played 2 matches.

Since A got only 1 point, they must have lost their match vs. B. ∴ A vs. B was 0–1, and B vs. C was 0–5.

A vs. C was a draw. And since A scored 3 goals and did not score any against B, A vs. C was 3–3.

Complete Solution

A vs. B	0–1
A vs. C	3–3
B vs. C	0–5

5. Soccer on the Island of Near Perfection

A drew 1 match, but since their goals for are not the same as their goals against, they must have played 2.

B got 1 point; ∴ they drew 1. But their goals for and against are different; ∴ they played 2; ∴ C also played 2 (for the matches played must be even).

C had 34 goals for; A and B had 46 + 50 goals against. 34 of those were scored by C, and the rest [(46 + 50) − 34 = 62] were scored against each other.

But A vs. B was a draw; ∴ the score must have been 31–31.

A had 58 goals for and 46 against; ∴ A vs. C was 27–15. And since C had 34 for and 36 against, ∴ C vs. B was 19–9.

Complete Solution

A vs. B	31–31
A vs. C	27–15
B vs. C	9–19

6. Uncle Bungle and the Use of Reason

The goals for of B, C, and D are 10 (4 + 6 + 0), and the goals against are 7 (3 + 3 + 1). ∴ A has played at least 1 match.

(i) Consider B. No matches lost or drawn, and goals are 4–3. ∴ B cannot have played 2 or more matches, for all would have been won, and the difference between goals for and goals against would have been more than 1. ∴ B played one match only, and the score was 4–3.

(ii) Consider D. No match could have been won, for no goals were scored. ∴ D played one match only, and the score was 0–1.

(iii) The total of matches played must be even (for each match appears twice). ∴ A played 2 matches (no teams can play more than 3). A and C must have played each other, and A played B or D, and C played B or D. But B match (4–3) cannot have been vs. C, who only had 3 goals against. ∴ B played A, and D played C.

So we have:

	A	B	C	D
A		3–4		X
B	4–3		X	X
C		X		1–0
D	X	X	0–1	

C's goals were 6–3; 1–0 vs. D, ∴ 5–3 vs. A.

Complete Solution

A vs. B	3–4
A vs. C	3–5
C vs. D	1–0

7. Nearly Right

Look first for the incorrect figure. If figures for C are correct, then C's points would be 2. But if points are correct, then C's points would be odd. ∴ either one of C's figures or one of the points figures must be wrong. ∴ all other figures must be correct.

A's figures cannot be right, for with no goals against, they cannot have lost a match. ∴ A must either have won 2 (4 points) or have won 1 and drawn 1 (3 points). ∴ A's points are incorrect; ∴ all other figures are correct. ∴ C's figures are correct; ∴ C must have won 1 and lost 1, and got 2 points. ∴ A's points must be odd, to make total of points even. ∴ A's points must be 3 (see above).

Total of points is (3 + 3 + 2 + 2) = 10. And since there are 2 points for each game, and each match appears twice (e.g., A vs. B is one of A's matches and one of B's), ∴ total of matches played must also be 10. ∴ B played 3 matches. ∴ all the matches were played except A vs. C (A and C only played 2 matches). A got 3 points; ∴ they drew 1 and won 1.

Suppose D got their 2 points from 2 draws; then they must have lost their third match (only 2 points). But this is not possible, for goals for are greater than goals against. ∴ D got their 2 points from a win, and they lost their other 2 matches. And A drew with B (0–0), and A vs. D was 4–0. D had 5 goals against. Four of them were scored by A; ∴ the other 1 must have been scored by B or by C, whichever beat them. And score in this match must have been 0–1. ∴ score in D's third match was 8–0. But this cannot have been vs. C, who only had 3 goals against. ∴ D vs. C must have been 0–1, and D vs. B was 8–0. And since C vs. D was 1–0. ∴ C vs. B was 2–3.

Complete Solution

A's points should be 3, not 2.

A vs. B	0–0
A vs. D	4–0
B vs. C	3–2
B vs. D	0–8
C vs. D	1–0

8. 5 Digits Divided by 2 Digits

```
            - - - -         (i)
    - - ) - - - - -         (ii)
        - -                 (iii)
        ___
        - - 2               (iv)
        - -                 (v)
        _____
            - - -           (vi)
            - - -           (vii)
```

Consider (iv), (v), and (vi):

(iv) must be 1 0 –, and (v) must be 9 –, since there is no figure in (vi) below the first figure in (v). (iii) must start with less than 9 [consider first figure in (iv)]. ∴ (v) must be the divisor times 2 or more.

If (v) is the divisor times 3, then the divisor is at most 33, and (v) would then be 99. ∴ the first figure of (vi) would be 3.

But $33 \times 9 = 297$; ∴ this is not possible (and if the divisor were less than 33 the situation would be worse).

∴ (v) is divisor times 2. If divisor were 48, then (v) would be 96 and (vi) would start with 6, which is not possible. ∴ divisor must be 49; ∴ (iii) is 49, (v) is 98, and (vi) and (vii) are 441 (the only multiple of 49 that starts with 4).

Add up from the bottom and we get:

Complete Solution

```
            1 2 0 9
    4 9 ) 5 9 2 4 1
          4 9
          ___
          1 0 2
            9 8
            _____
              4 4 1
              4 4 1
              =====
```

9. 4 Digits Divided by 2 Digits

```
           - - -                    (i)
      - - ) 6 - - -                 (ii)
           - -                      (iii)
           ‾‾‾‾
           - - -                    (iv)
           - - 3                    (v)

             - -                    (vi)
             - 4                    (vii)
             ‾‾‾
```

From (v), the divisor must be odd. ∴ (vii) must be the divisor times 2, at least. First figure in (vii) cannot be 1 (the divisor would then be 7); nor 2 (the divisor would then be 12, but it must be odd); nor 4 [the divisor would then be 11, and (v) would not be possible]; nor 6 (all the factors of 64 are even). ∴ (vii) must be 34 (17 × 2), 54 (27 × 2), 74 (37 × 2), 84 (21 × 4), or 94 (47 × 2).

If (vii) were 84 (21 × 4), the divisor would be 21 and (v) would be 63, which is not possible.

All the other divisors end in 7; ∴ (v) must be 9 times the divisor (7 × 9 = 63).

If (vii) were 54, the divisor would be 27; ∴ (iii) would be 54; ∴ (iv) would start with 1, and (v) could not be 27 × 9 (243). ∴ (vii) is not 54.

If (vii) were 74, divisor would be 37; (v) would be 333 (37 × 9), (iv) would be 340, (iii) would be 37, and the first figure of (ii) would be 7 (not 6, figure given). ∴ (vii) is not 74.

If (vii) were 94, the divisor would be 47. First figure in (v) would be 2 (at most); but 47 × 9 = 423. ∴ (vii) is not 94.

∴ (vii) must be 34, and the divisor must be 17.

(v) must be 153 (17 × 9), and (iii) must be 51 (17 × 3).

Add up from the bottom and we get:

$$17 \overline{)\begin{array}{r} 392 \\ 6664 \\ 51 \\ \hline 156 \\ 153 \\ \hline 34 \\ 34 \\ \hline\hline \end{array}}$$

10. 1 of Each

Suppose C's remark is true. Then A's remark is true, and B is a Shilli-Shalla. But this is not possible, for we know that one of them is a Wotta-Woppa. ∴ C's remark must be false.

∴ A's remark is not true; and since A and C have both made false statements, ∴ B must be a Pukka.

∴ B's remark is true, and C is not a Shilli-Shalla; ∴ A must be a Shilli-Shalla and C must be a Wotta-Woppa.

Complete Solution

Alf is a Shilli-Shalla.
Bert is a Pukka.
Charlie is a Wotta-Woppa.

11. Silly, Silent C?

If A's statement were true, then A could only be a Shilli-Shalla. Then B would have to be a Pukka. But this is not possible, for B says that he is a Shilli-Shalla. ∴ A's statement cannot be true.

∴ A does *not* belong to a less truthful tribe than B does. ∴ A belongs to a more truthful tribe than B does.

But since A makes a false statement, A must be a Shilli-Shalla. ∴ B's statement is false. ∴ B can only be a Wotta-Woppa. ∴ C must be a Pukka.

Complete Solution

A is a Shilli-Shalla.
B is a Wotta-Woppa.
C is a Pukka.

12. The Door Men Come to the Island

Suppose C1 is true. Then A is a Wotta-Woppa. ∴ from A1, B is a Shilli-Shalla. ∴ C would be a Pukka. But C2 would not then be true. ∴ C1 is not true.

∴ B1 is false (for C2 is false).

∴ A must be a Pukka (no one else can be).

∴ From A1, B is not a Shilli-Shalla. ∴ C is a Shilli-Shalla and B is a Wotta-Woppa.

A2 is true; ∴ C is the Door-Knob-Polisher.

And since B2 is false, A is not the Door-Opener. ∴ B is the Door-Opener. And A is the Door-Shutter.

Complete Solution

A is a Pukka and is the Door-Shutter.
B is a Wotta-Woppa and is the Door-Opener.
C is a Shilli-Shalla and is the Door-Knob-Polisher.

13. The Bumbling B

(i) Suppose C1 is true. Then B would, quite rightly, say that A belonged to the Shilli-Shalla. ∴ B has made a true statement, and A is a Shilli-Shalla. ∴ there is no Wotta-Woppa. But we are told that one of them is a Wotta-Woppa; ∴ our assumption is wrong, and C1 is false.

(ii) If A1 is false, then B is a Wotta-Woppa; ∴ none of them can be a Pukka. But we are told that one of them is. ∴ A1 is true.

(iii) B is not a Wotta-Woppa, and A is not (for A has made a true statement); ∴ C is a Wotta-Woppa.

(iv) If A is a Shilli-Shalla, then B would be a Pukka, and C1 would be true. But we know that C1 is not true. ∴ A is a Pukka, and B is a Shilli-Shalla.

Complete Solution

A is a Pukka.
B is a Shilli-Shalla.
C is a Wotta-Woppa.

14. Imperfect Birthdays

Suppose B1 is true. Then D1 would be true, and A would be a Wotta-Woppa. ∴ A2 would be false; ∴ B3 (and ∴ B1) would not be true. But this is not possible; ∴ B1 cannot be true. ∴ D is not a Pukka, and A2 is false. ∴ C is a Pukka (no one else can be).

From C2 (true), A must be a Shilli-Shalla and D must be a Wotta-Woppa.

From A1 (true) and C1 (true), all birthdays are multiples of 6.

But from B3 (false) not the 30th. ∴ birthdays are on 6th, 12th, 18th, and 24th; ∴ B2 is false; ∴ B is a Wotta-Woppa.

And from A3 (true), B's birthday is on the 6th from C3 (true), C's birthday is on the 24th, and D's is on the 12th.

∴ A's must be on the 18th.

Complete Solution

A is a Shilli-Shalla, and his birthday is on the 18th of April.
B is a Wotta-Woppa, and his birthday is on the 6th of April.
C is a Pukka, and his birthday is on the 24th of April.
D is a Wotta-Woppa, and his birthday is on the 12th of April.

15. How Many of Each?

Suppose C1 is true. Then B is a Pukka. $\therefore$ B2 is true, and A never tells the truth. $\therefore$ A2 is false and C is a Wotta-Woppa.

But this is not possible, for C1 is true. $\therefore$ C cannot be a Wotta-Woppa. $\therefore$ C1 cannot be true, and B is not a Pukka.

Since C1 is false, $\therefore$ C2 is false (C cannot be a Pukka). $\therefore$ C is a Wotta-Woppa. $\therefore$ A2 is false.

$\therefore$ A1 cannot be true—for if it were, A would not be a Wotta-Woppa. $\therefore$ A is a Wotta-Woppa.

$\therefore$ B2 is true. And since from C1 (false), B is not a Pukka, B must be a Shilli-Shalla.

$\therefore$ B1 is false, and A is not older than B.

Complete Solution

A is not older than B.
A is a Wotta-Woppa.
B is a Shilli-Shalla.
C is a Wotta-Woppa.

16. Wine Comes to the Island

Suppose B2 were true. Then D1 would be true. ∴ A and C would be Wotta-Woppas (according to our assumption no one else can be). ∴ C2 would be false. But C2 should then be true. ∴ our assumption is wrong, and B2 is false. ∴ either A or C or both must be a Pukka.

Suppose that A2 is true. Then D1 would be false, and A and C would be Pukkas, but this is not possible, for C2 could not then be true. ∴ A2 is false. ∴ C must be a Pukka, for D cannot be (see B2). ∴ from C2, A is a Wotta-Woppa. ∴ A2 is false, and the wine man is not a Pukka.

From A1 (false), B is a Wotta-Woppa. ∴ the wine man is A or B. But from B1 (false), he cannot be B. ∴ A is the wine man.

∴ D must be a Shilli-Shalla, and since D1 is true, D2 must be false.

From C1 (true), C purchased 2 bottles.

From D2 (false), D did not purchase 3 bottles. ∴ D must have purchased 1 bottle. ∴ B must have purchased 3 bottles.

Complete Solution

A is a Wotta-Woppa and is the wine man.
B is a Wotta-Woppa and purchased 3 bottles.
C is a Pukka and purchased 2 bottles.
D is a Shilli-Shalla and purchased 1 bottle.

17. A Wink and a Nod

Suppose A1 is true. Then A would be a Pukka. ∴ B1 would be false (only 1 Pukka). Since we are assuming that A is a Pukka, ∴ from A2 ("the lower the truer"), B2 is false. ∴ B would be a Wotta-Woppa. ∴ C would be a Shilli-Shalla. But according to our assumption (A2 is true), C1 would be true. And according to our assumption C2 is true. ∴ C would be a Pukka. But this is not possible. ∴ Our assumption was wrong, and A1 is false.

∴ A is a Shilli-Shalla. ∴ A2 is true. ∴ "the lower the truer." ∴ C1 is false (for A's number is between B's and C's). ∴ B is a Pukka (no one else could be). ∴ C is a Wotta-Woppa.

From B2, B's number is 1. From A3 (false), A's number is 6 or more. ∴ from B3 (true), C's number is a perfect square and is greater than A's, which is "6 or more." ∴ C's number is 9. ∴ from C3 (false), A's number is 7.

Complete Solution

A is a Shilli-Shalla, and his number is 7.
B is a Pukka, and his number is 1.
C is a Wotta-Woppa, and his number is 9.

18. Some Old Men on the Island

Suppose C1 is true. Then C3 is true (whether C is a Pukka or a Shilli-Shalla); ∴ B2 is true. But if C1 is true, this is not possible. ∴ C1 cannot be true. ∴ C3 is false. ∴ B2 is false. ∴ A must be older than C.

Suppose A3 is false. Then D does not belong to a more truthful tribe than A. ∴ D cannot be a Pukka. ∴ if A3 is false, no one could be a Pukka. ∴ A3 must be true. ∴ D must be a Pukka, and A must be a Shilli-Shalla.

Since D2 is true, D's age minus A's age = 12; and since A1 is true, A's age is a multiple of 6, D's age is even, and C2 is true. ∴ C is a Shilli-Shalla; ∴ B must be a Wotta-Woppa (no one else can be).

Since D3 is true, C's age is a multiple of 13. Suppose it was 13. Then from D1 (true), B's age would be 39. But this is not possible, for from A1 (true), we know that A's age is a multiple of 6, and from A2 (false), we know that A's age is the same as B's.

Suppose C's age is 26. Then A's age and B's age would both be 78; and from D2 (true), D's age would be 90. And it is easy to see that this is the only possible answer.

Complete Solution

A is a Shilli-Shalla, and his age is 78.
B is a Wotta-Woppa, and his age is 78.
C is a Shilli-Shalla, and his age is 26.
D is a Pukka, and his age is 90.

19. On the Silly Side of Silly Street

Consider D2. If this were true, then B would be a Pukka and D would be a Shilli-Shalla. ∴ A2 would be false.

If C1 were true, then A and C would both be Shilli-Shallas (not Pukkas, for A2 is false). But there is only one Shilli-Shalla.

If C1 were false, then A and C would not belong to the same tribe. ∴ A or C would be a Shilli-Shalla (according to our assumption that they have both made a false statement). But this is not possible, for we are assuming that D is a Shilli-Shalla, and we know that there is only one Shilli-Shalla. ∴ our assumption must be false. ∴ D2 is not true.

∴ B's tribe is as truthful or less truthful than D's. ∴ either D is a Shilli-Shalla and B is a Shilli-Shalla, OR D is a Shilli-Shalla and B is a Wotta-Woppa, OR D is a Wotta-Woppa and B is a Wotta-Woppa.

But the first of these is not possible, for there would then be 2 Shilli-Shallas; ∴ B is a Wotta-Woppa.

If C1 were true, then A and C would both be Pukkas (at least one from each tribe). ∴ D would be a Shilli-Shalla (at least one from each tribe). But A2 would then be false; ∴ C1 would be false. ∴ A is a Pukka (no one else can be). ∴ from A2, D is a Wotta-Woppa. ∴ C is a Shilli-Shalla. ∴ C2 is true, and A lives in No. 35.

B2 is false; ∴ C's number is greater than A's (they cannot be equal). ∴ C must be 37, 39, or 41. But from A1 (true), C is a multiple of 3; ∴ C is 39 and D is 13.

From D1 (false), B's number is greater than C's; ∴ B's number must be 41.

Complete Solution

A is a Pukka and lives at No. 35.
B is a Wotta-Woppa and lives at No. 41.
C is a Shilli-Shalla and lives at No. 39.
D is a Wotta-Woppa and lives at No. 13.

20. The Poorer the Truer

(i) Suppose C3 is true (∴ C1 is also true). ∴ B is more truthful (because wages are less).

∴ B must make 3 true remarks; ∴ is a Pukka. ∴ B2 ("I am a Shilli-Shalla") is false. But this is a contradiction. ∴ our assumption must be false. ∴ C3 is false. ∴ C1 is also false.

(ii) Since C3 is false and wages are all different, ∴ B's wages are more than C's; ∴ B is less truthful than C; ∴ B's remarks are all false; ∴ C's remarks not all false; ∴ C2 is true (we already know that C1 and C3 are false).

(iii) A diagram will help.

A:	1. ✔	C:	1. X
	2.		2. ✔
	3. ✔		3. X
B:	1. X	D:	1. ✔
	2. X		2.
	3. X		3. ✔

We see from this that either A or D is a Pukka (all remarks true), and the other one must be a Shilli-Shalla with first and third remarks true. ∴ A1, A3, D1, and D3 are all true, and one only of A2 and D2 is true. (This information has been inserted in diagram.)

(iv) A diagram giving information about wives and wages will also help.

Wages		X	Y	Z	Bachelor
	A		X		
24, 30	B	X	✔	X	X
	C		X		X
16, 20, 24, 28	D		X		

(v) We know that A1 is true.

$$\frac{\text{B's (Wotta-Woppa's) wages}}{\text{one of Shilli-Shallas's wages}} = \frac{120}{100} = \frac{6}{5}$$

∴ B's wages are a multiple of 6; ∴ they must be 18, 24, or 30. And ∴ one of the Shilli-Shallas's wages must be 15, 20, or 25. But not 15, for this is the lowest pay possible; ∴ only a Pukka could have this pay. ∴ B's wages are 24 or 30, and one of the Shilli-Shallas's wages are 20 or 25.

(vi) From A3 (true), D's wages must be 16, 20, 24, or 28.

(vii) From B3 (false), B (Wotta-Woppa, best paid) is *not* married to X.

(viii) From D3 (true), B is *not* married to Z.

(ix) From C2 (true), the Pukka is a bachelor; ∴ neither B nor C is a bachelor. ∴ by elimination B is married to Y. (The information discovered so far has been inserted in diagram).

(x) From B1 (false), Z's husband's wages are odd; ∴ Z's husband is *not* D.

(xi) Consider A2. Suppose this is true. Then B's wages must be 30 (not 24, for A's would then be 14, which is not possible). ∴ A's wages must be 20. And from 5, if B's wages are 30, then one of the Shilli-Shallas's is 25. But in this case wages are 20; 30; 25; 16; 20, 24, or 28; and D1 is false. But we know that D1 must be true. ∴ our assumption is false and A2 cannot be true; ∴ A is a Shilli-Shalla and D is a Pukka.

(xii) From D2 (true), the wages of the Shilli-Shallas differ by 1 hope. From A1 (true), the wages of one of the Shilli-Shallas is 20 hopes or 25 hopes (see 5). From D1 (true), someone's wages are a prime number of hopes. But this cannot be B or D or one of the Shilli-Shallas (20 or 25 hopes); ∴ it must be the other Shilli-Shalla. But if the wages of one Shilli-Shalla are 25 hopes, then wages of the other would be an even number; ∴ not prime. ∴ wages of one Shilli-Shalla are 20 hopes and of the other 19 hopes. ∴ the less truthful Shilli-Shalla (C) has wages of 20 hopes, and the other (A) has wages of 19 hopes. ∴ the wages of the Wotta-Woppa (B) are 24 hopes. ∴ the wages of the Pukka (D) (16, 20, 24, or 28) can only be 16 hopes.

(xiii) From C2 (true), D is a bachelor. From B1 (false), Z's husband cannot be C. ∴ Z is married to A. And by elimination C is married to X.

Complete Solution

A is a Shilli-Shalla (more truthful), his wages are 19 hopes per week, and he is married to Z.

B is a Wotta-Woppa, his wages are 24 hopes per week, and he is married to Y.

C is a Shilli-Shalla (less truthful), his wages are 20 hopes per week, and he is married to X.

D is a Pukka, his wages are 16 hopes per week, and he is a bachelor.

21. What the Secretaries Said

(i) B cannot have played 1 and won 2; C cannot have played 2, won 2, and lost 2; ∴ A must be a Pukka. ∴ B's won must be false, for if B won 2, then A would have lost a match. If B is a Shilli-Shalla, then B's played and B's lost would both be true, but this is not possible, for B cannot have played 1 and lost 2. ∴ B is a Wotta-Woppa; ∴ C is a Shilli-Shalla.

(ii) Since B's played is false, ∴ B must have played 2; ∴ C must have played 2 (to make total of matches played even). ∴ C's played, lost, and goals for are correct, and B's won, drawn, and goals against are incorrect.

(iii) Since C lost both their matches and scored *no* goals, we have:

	A	B	C
A		*Drawn*	*Won* −0
B	*Drawn*		*Won* −0
C	*Lost* 0−	*Lost* 0−	

We know that A had 2 goals against but none by C. ∴ A vs. B must have been 2–2, and A vs. C, 1–0. B scored 2 goals vs. A and at least 1 vs. C (match was won). But C vs. B cannot be 0–1, for C's goals against are given as 2, and we know this is wrong. And B vs. C cannot be 2–0, for B's goals for are given as 4, and we know that this is wrong. ∴ B vs. C was 3–0 ("In no case did a team win by a majority of more than 3 goals").

Complete Solution

A vs. B	2–2
A vs. C	1–0
B vs. C	3–0

22. Soccer Makes Us Less Imperfect

We must first try to find the tribes to which A, B, and C belong. Let us try to find the Pukka.

A cannot be a Pukka, for A played 1 and lost 2, which is not possible. C cannot be a Pukka, for they won 1 but only got 1 point. ∴ B must be the Pukka, and their figures are correct.

Suppose C is a Wotta-Woppa. Then they must have played 1 (they cannot have played 0, for B must have played A and C). And C would have won 0, lost 0, and drawn 1. But in that case C would have got 1 point, but this is the figure given. ∴ C must be a Shilli-Shalla, and A must be a Wotta-Woppa.

We now have to find out whether C starts with a true or a false statement. Suppose C's played is false; then it would be 1. The total of matches played must be even; ∴ A's played would be 1 (figure given). But this is not possible, for A is a Wotta-Woppa. ∴ C's played must be correct. ∴ C won 0, lost 1, and drew 1.

We now know that A won at least 1; ∴ they cannot have drawn 2. ∴ since A's drawn is given as 1, it must be 0. ∴ B vs. C was a draw.

∴ we have:

	A	B	C
A	X	*Lost*	*Won*
B	*Won*	X	*Drawn*
C	*Lost*	*Drawn*	X

Since C's played is correct and C is a Shilli-Shalla, ∴ C's goals for (0) is correct. ∴ B vs. C was 0–0, and C vs. A was 0 – ? ∴ B vs. A was 4–1. A vs. C cannot be 1–0, for A's goals for would then be correct. And A vs. C cannot be 2–0, for C's goals against would then be correct. And since we are told that in no case was a match won by a margin of more than 3 goals, ∴ A vs. C must be 3–0.

A vs. B	1–4
A vs. B	3–0
B vs. C	0–0

23. We Try Letters for Digits

Let us first try to find the Pukka.

Consider A. *m* (A's played) cannot be more than 2. And *y, k,* and *d* should then all be less than 2. But that is not possible. ∴ A is not the Pukka.

Consider C. *x* (C's played) cannot be 0, for in that case *d* (C's wins) would not also be 0. And *x* cannot be 1 or 2 (see C's lost and drawn). ∴ C is not the Pukka.

∴ B is the Pukka. ∴ *m* (B's played) must be 2, *x* must be 1, and *y* must be 0. ∴ *k* and *d* (A's lost and drawn) are both more than 2. ∴ they are both wrong. ∴ A is a Wotta-Woppa. ∴ C is a Shilli-Shalla.

Since A's played is wrong, it can only be 1 (*x*). ∴ since the total of games must be even, C's played (*x*) is correct. ∴ C lost 1, has 0 goals for, and got no points. ∴ C vs. B was 0–?.

B had 2 goals for and 2 against. ∴ B vs. A was ?–2.

We know that A did not have 0 goals against (figure given); ∴ they must have had 1 (not 2, for B vs. A was not a draw). ∴ B vs. A was 1–2, and B vs. C was 1–0.

Complete Solution

A vs. B	2–1
B vs. C	1–0

24. Uncle Bungle Gets Things Right

Let us first try to find the Pukka.

Consider A. g (A's played) must be greater than h or k. ∴ g must be 2. But it would not be possible for h to be 1 and k to be 0, for A would then only have played 1. If h were 0 and k were 1, then A would have got only 1 point. But g (A's points) should stand for 2. ∴ A cannot be the Pukka.

B cannot be the Pukka, for k, y, t, and g cannot all be 2 or less. ∴ C must be the Pukka. And since g must be greater than k and h, g must be 2.

Since C cannot lose 1 and win and draw none, ∴ k must be 1 and h must be 0. ∴ since C won 1 and drew 1, p (C's points) must be 3.

Consider B. Since y and t are consecutive letters and stand for a digit that is more than 3, ∴ B is the Wotta-Woppa. ∴ A is the Shilli-Shalla.

Since k (B's played) is wrong and $k = 1$, ∴ B must have played 2. ∴ since the total of matches played must be even, A played 2. ∴ A's played is correct. ∴ A's points are also correct.

∴ A got 2 (g) points, and since A lost 1, they drew none.

∴ C's drawn match was vs. B. And since C had no goals against (h), B vs. C was 0–0.

∴ since C had p (3) goals for, C vs. A was 3–0.

We know that A had k (1) goal for, ∴ A vs. B was 1–?.

But since A won this match, the score can only have been 1–0.

Complete Solution

A is a Shilli-Shalla.	A vs. B	1–0
B is a Wotta-Woppa.	A vs. C	0–3
C is a Pukka.	B vs. C	0–0

25. A Couple of Pukkas

Let us first try to find out which teams are Pukkas.

D cannot play t and win t, for either y or m (D's lost and drawn) must be at least 1. $\therefore$ D is not a Pukka.

A similar argument applies to A. $\therefore$ B and C are the Pukkas.

Consider C. t (C's played) must be greater than p, g, or m. $\therefore$ t must be 3. (It cannot be more.) And p, g, and m must be 0, 1, and 2, but we do not yet know which is which. And k (C's points) must be 4, 5, or 6. But k cannot be 6, for wins would then be t (i.e., 3). $\therefore$ $k = 4$ or 5.

Consider B. m (B's played) must be 1 or 2. And since B's lost is also m, B lost every match. $\therefore$ g (B's points) is 0.

Consider D. Suppose D is a Shilli-Shalla and that D's played is correct. Then D's lost should also be correct. But this is not possible, for we know that y is more than 3. Suppose D's played is wrong (and D's played is less than 3); then D's wins would also be wrong (t). $\therefore$ D must be the Wotta-Woppa. $\therefore$ A is the Shilli-Shalla.

Consider A. A's draws 3 (t) cannot be correct, for we know that B drew none (g). $\therefore$ A's first statement (played m) must be correct. We know that m (A's played) must be 1 or 2.

Suppose $m = 2$. Then A got m (2) points. They cannot have won 1 and lost 1, for we know that they lost none (g). $\therefore$ they would have had to have drawn 2. C would also have drawn 2 (m). And since B drew none, D would have had to have drawn 2 (not 0, for A and C would then have had to play each other twice). But 2 (m) is given as D's draws, and D is a Wotta-Woppa.

$\therefore$ m cannot be 2; $\therefore$ $m = 1$ and $p = 2$. $\therefore$ k (C's points) = 5.

Since the total of matches played is even, and A, B, and C played 1, 1, and 3, D must have played 1.

A played 1 and drew 1 and scored 3 goals. $\therefore$ A vs. C was 3–3. B vs. C was 0–5 (figure given).

And since x (C's goals for) cannot be more than 9, C vs. D can only be 1–0. And $x = 9$.

A vs. C	3–3
B vs. C	0–5
C vs. D	1–0

26. C Is Silent

The only way in which the truth-telling rules of the Jokers can be different from those of the other three tribes is for their first and third statements to have different truth values—that is, one must be false and the other true. The second statement could be true or false.

Suppose that D1 is true. Then A is a Pukka; ∴ A1 is true; ∴ D would also be a Pukka. But there is only one Pukka. ∴ D1 cannot be true.

If D3 were true, then D would be a Joker; but if D3 is true, then B would be a Joker; ∴ D3 cannot be true.

∴ D must be a Shilli-Shalla or a Wotta-Woppa. ∴ D2 is true and D is a Shilli-Shalla.

∴ B1 is false; ∴ A1 is false; ∴ C must be a Pukka (no one else can be).

And from D3 (false), B is not a Joker; ∴ A must be a Joker; ∴ B must be a Wotta-Woppa.

Complete Solution

A is a Joker.
B is a Wotta-Woppa.
C is a Pukka.
D is a Shilli-Shalla.

27. All Four of Us Are Here

Suppose C1 is true. Then A is a Wotta-Woppa. Therefore A1 is false; therefore D is a Pukka; therefore D1 is true; therefore B is a Wotta-Woppa.

But this would mean that A and B are both Wotta-Woppas, but we are told that there is 1 representative of each tribe. Therefore C1 cannot be true, and A is not a Wotta-Woppa.

Since B3 and C1 are false, B1 is true; ∴ B is a Joker; ∴ D1 is false; ∴ A is a Pukka (no one else can be).

And since A2 is true, C must be a Shilli-Shalla and D a Wotta-Woppa. And B2 is true.

Complete Solution

A is a Pukka.
B is a Joker.
C is a Shilli-Shalla.
D is a Wotta-Woppa.

28. A Was Absent

The only way that the truth-telling rules of the Jokers can be different from those of the other 3 tribes is for their first and third statements to have different truth values: that is, one must be false and the other true. The second statement could be true or false.

Suppose B3 is true. Then D is a Pukka; ∴ D1 is true; ∴ B is a Joker; ∴ B1 is true. But if B1 and B3 are both true, then B cannot be a Joker; ∴ B3 cannot be true. ∴ it is not possible for B to be a Joker; ∴ B3 must be false; ∴ D is not a Pukka. ∴ A or C is a Pukka.

Suppose C1 is false; then A is not a Pukka. And in that case, no one could be a Pukka; ∴ C1 must be true, and A is a Pukka.

We know that B2 is true; ∴ B is a Shilli-Shalla.

∴ C must be a Joker, and D must be a Wotta-Woppa.

Complete Solution

A is a Pukka.
B is a Shilli-Shalla.
C is a Joker.
D is a Wotta-Woppa.

29. The Jokers Play Soccer

Let us first try to find the Pukka: It cannot be A, for if they lost 2, they could not have no goals against. It cannot be B, for they could not have played 1 and drawn 2. It cannot be D, for if they drew 1, they could not have no points. ∴ C must be the Pukka.

And since they had 4 goals for and 2 against, they must have won 2 and drawn 1 (each match that was won was won by 1 goal). It is not possible for A to have lost 2, for if both their goals were wrong, it would be 0–1. ∴ A must have lost 1, and A must be a Wotta-Woppa. And A vs. C is 0–1. And since their goals were 0–1, they can only have played 1 match.

We know that B or D is a Shilli-Shalla; ∴ one of them must have played only 1 match (the Shilli-Shalla started with a true statement). ∴ since the total of matches played must be even, A, B, and D all played 1 match only vs. C.

∴ B's played is correct, and B's drawn must be 1.

∴ B's points are wrong. ∴ B is a Joker. ∴ D is a Shilli-Shalla. B drew 1; ∴ B vs. C was a draw.

If B vs. C was 2–2, then C vs. D would be 1–0 as well as C vs. A. ∴ B vs. C can only be 1–1, and C vs. D is 2–1.

Complete Solution

A is a Wotta-Woppa.	A vs. C	0–1
B is a Joker.	B vs. C	1–1
C is a Pukka.	C vs. D	2–1
D is a Shilli-Shalla.		

30. C Was Far from Silent

The only way that the truth-telling rules of the Jokers can be different from those of the other 3 tribes is for their first and third statements to have different truth values—that is, one must be false and the other true. The second statement could be true or false.

If C1 were true, then B would be a Pukka and C3 would be false, for if B is a Pukka, C cannot be. If C1 were false, then C3 would be false, for if C makes a false statement he cannot be a Pukka. ∴ C3 must be false. ∴ D1 is false.

If B1 were true, then A would be a Pukka (no one else can be). And if B1 were false, A would have to be a Pukka, for all the other 3 have made a false statement. ∴ A is a Pukka.

∴ C1 is false and C is a Wotta-Woppa or a Shilli-Shalla. But from A1 (true), C is a Shilli-Shalla. ∴ C2 is true; ∴ B cannot be a Wotta-Woppa. ∴ B must be a Joker. ∴ D is a Wotta-Woppa.

Complete Solution

    A is a Pukka.
    B is a Joker.
    C is a Shilli-Shalla.
    D is a Wotta-Woppa.

31. Our Factory on the Island

If B1 were true, then C1 would be false. ∴ A would be a Pukka. ∴ A2 would be true. But if it were true, then A could not be a Pukka. ∴ our assumption must be wrong, and B1 must be false. ∴ D3 is true. And since B1 is false, C is not a Wotta-Woppa. ∴ either A or B must be a Wotta-Woppa.

Suppose that A was a Wotta-Woppa. Then A2 would be false, and D would not make more true statements than A. But we know what D makes 1 true statement (D3). ∴ A cannot be a Wotta-Woppa. ∴ B must be a Wotta-Woppa. ∴ B3 is false. ∴ D is not a Joker. And since D3 is true, ∴ D1 is true (for D is not a Joker).

Suppose C1 was false. Then A would be a Pukka, and A2 would be true. ∴ D would make more true statements than A. But this is not possible. ∴ C1 must be true. From D1 (true), A is a Joker. ∴ C1 is true, and since A is a Joker, C's first and third statements have the same truth value. ∴ the Shilli-Shalla is the Sweeper-Upper.

∴ neither A nor B is the Sweeper-Upper. We know that B2 is false; ∴ A is not the Worker. ∴ since A is a Joker, A3 is true. ∴ the Pukka is the Door-Opener.

And since the Joker's first statement is false, ∴ D2 is true, and D is the Pukka. ∴ C is the Shilli-Shalla. And since D is a Pukka, A2 is true. The Joker (A) is the Door-Opener (no one else can be).

∴ B is the Worker (no one else can be). And C (Shilli-Shalla) is the Sweeper-Upper.

Complete Solution

Alf is the Door-Shutter, and he is a Joker.
Bert is the Worker, and he is a Wotta-Woppa.
Charlie is the Sweeper-Upper, and he is a Shilli-Shalla.
Duggie is the Door-Opener, and he is a Pukka.

32. The Joke That Did Not Amuse

We are told that the truth-telling rules of the Jokers are different from those of the other 3 tribes. The only way that this can happen is for the Jokers's first and third statements to have different truth values—that is, one must be false and the other true. The second one could be false or true.

B1 and B3 cannot both be true or both false; ∴ B must be a Joker. But we do not know which is true and which is false, and we do not know whether B2 is true or false.

Since B is a Joker, C3 is true; ∴ C1 is true. And B's shack number must be between 31 and 35 (inclusive).

Consider D3. If true, then A makes at least 2 true statements. And in that case all 4 of them would make at least 1 true statement. But this is not possible, for we know that one of them is a Wotta-Woppa; ∴ D2 cannot be true; ∴ D1 cannot be true.

And since D3 is false, A cannot be a Pukka; ∴ C must be a Pukka (no one else can be). ∴ C1 and C2 are true.

D3 is false; ∴ A must be a Wotta-Woppa and D must be a Shilli-Shalla. ∴ D2 is true.

We know that C is a Pukka; ∴ B3 is false and B1 is true. And from A3 (false), B2 is true.

We know that B's shack is between 31 and 35 (inclusive). ∴ from D2 (true), it must be 35.

From A1 (false), A's shack has a higher number than C's, and from D1 (false), D's shack has a higher number than A's. ∴ D's shack is between 21 and 30, A's shack is between 11 and 20, and C's shack is between 1 and 10.

From C2 (true), C's shack must be 3, 6, or 9. And from A2 (false), it must be even. ∴ C's shack is 6. From C1 (true), A's shack must be 14.

From B2 (true), D's shack is a multiple of 14; ∴ D's shack is 28.

Complete Solution

A is a Wotta-Woppa; his shack number is 14.
B is a Joker; his shack number is 35.
C is a Pukka; his shack number is 6.
D is a Shilli-Shalla; his shack number is 28.

33. Reading Comes to the Island

We are told that the truth-telling rules of the Jokers, in making 3 statements, are different from those of the other 3 tribes. The only way that this can happen is for the Jokers's first and third statements to have different truth values—that is, one must be false and the other must be true. The second one could be false or true.

Suppose C3 is true. Then B is a Wotta-Woppa, and B3 is false. ∴ A is a Pukka. ∴ A2 is true, and D is not a Joker. ∴ C would be the Joker. ∴ C1 should be false—for the Jokers's first and third statements have different truth values. But according to our assumption, it would be true. ∴ our assumption is wrong and C3 must be false. ∴ B is not a Wotta-Woppa.

Suppose A is a Pukka. Then from A1, C would be a Shilli-Shalla. And from A2, D would not be a Joker. ∴ B would be the Joker, and D would be the Wotta-Woppa. ∴ according to our assumption, D3 should then be false. But if B is a Joker, D3 would be true. ∴ our assumption is wrong, and A is not a Pukka. ∴ B3 is true; ∴ D3 is true.

Suppose A1 is true. Then C would be a Shilli-Shalla. And since we are assuming that they have all made at least 1 true statement, no one could be a Wotta-Woppa. ∴ A1 cannot be true. ∴ C is not a Shilli-Shalla. ∴ B1 is true.

Suppose D1 were false. Then B would be a Shilli-Shalla, and D would be a Joker. But this is not possible, for neither A nor C could be a Pukka. ∴ D1 must be true, and B is not a Shilli-Shalla. And since D is not a Joker, A2 is true. A, B, and D have all made true statements; ∴ C must be the Wotta-Woppa. ∴ A must be the Joker (no one else can be). ∴ A3 is true.

From D1 (true), B is not a Shilli-Shalla. ∴ B must be a Pukka. ∴ D must be a Shilli-Shalla, and D2 is false.

From A3 (true), 8 books were sold all together.

From B2 (true), B bought 4 of them.

And since B, C, and D all bought at least 1 book, and each bought a different number, and C2 is false, D did not buy 1; ∴ C must have purchased 1, and D must have purchased 3.

A is a Joker.

B is a Pukka; he purchased 4 books.

C is a Wotta-Woppa; he purchased 1 book.

D is a Shilli-Shalla; he purchased 3 books.

34. How Was the Joker's Logic?

The only way that the truth-telling rules of the Jokers can be different from those of the other 3 tribes is for their first and third statements to have different truth values—that is, one must be false and the other true. The second statement could be true or false.

Suppose that D1 was true. Then A would be a Pukka and B would be a Joker (A1 true), and C would be a Wotta-Woppa (no one else can be). But according to our assumption, C2 is true. ∴ our assumption is wrong, and D1 is false.

Suppose that C was a Pukka. Then A would be a Wotta-Woppa (C1 true) and D would be a Shilli-Shalla (C2 true). ∴ B would be a Joker. But from A1 (false), B is not a Joker. ∴ C is not a Pukka. From D1 (false), A is not a Pukka. ∴ B must be a Pukka (no one else can be). From B1 (true), one of C's statements is true.

Suppose that C1 were false. Then A is not a Wotta-Woppa, and since C2 would then be true, D would be a Shilli-Shalla. ∴ C would be a Wotta-Woppa (no one else can be). But this is contrary to our assumption. ∴ our assumption is wrong, and C1 must be true, and C2 false. ∴ A is a Wotta-Woppa. And since D is not a Shilli-Shalla, C must be a Shilli-Shalla, and D must be a Joker.

Since A2 is false, ∴ D2 is true. ∴ C was higher in the logic test than A was. And from B2 (true), the Wotta-Woppa (A) was 2 places higher than the Pukka (B) in the logic test. Since C was higher than A, and A was 2 places higher than B, we can only have:

1.	C	Shilli-Shalla
2.	A	Wotta-Woppa
3.	D	Joker
4.	B	Pukka

	LOGIC TEST
A was a Wotta-Woppa.	1. Shilli-Shalla
B was a Pukka.	2. Wotta-Woppa
C was a Shilli-Shalla.	3. Joker
D was a Joker.	4. Pukka

35. Only One Joker—but What About the Other Tribes?

Suppose B1 is true. Then C is a Pukka, and A is a Wotta-Woppa. And since A1 would then be false, D would not be a Joker. ∴ B would have to be a Joker. ∴ B3 must (according to our assumption) be false. ∴ B is not a Joker, and there would be no Joker. ∴ B1 must be false, and B3 could be true or false (as far as we know yet).

Suppose A1 is true. Then B3 would be false. And B would be a Wotta-Woppa or a Shilli-Shalla. And if A1 is true, then C2 would be false, and D1 would be true. But we know that D3 is true. ∴ D cannot be a Joker. ∴ our assumption is wrong, and A1 is false.

Suppose B is the Joker. Then B3 would be true and D1 would be false. But in that case D would be a Joker, for D3 is true. But we know that there is only one Joker. ∴ B is not the Joker. ∴ B3 is false.

And since D is not the Joker, D1 is true. ∴ D makes at least 2 true statements, and B cannot make more than 1 true statement. .. A3 is true. And since we know that A1 is false, ∴ A is the Joker. ∴ C2 is false. ∴ A, B, and C all make at least 1 false statement. ∴ since D makes at least 2 true statements, C1 is true. ∴ C is a Shilli-Shalla.

D2 cannot be true, for if it were, D would be a Pukka, and we know that B and C are not Pukkas. ∴ D2 is false. ∴ D is a Shilli-Shalla. ∴ since "3 of us do not belong to the same tribe," B cannot be a Shilli-Shalla. ∴ B2 is false, and B is a Wotta-Woppa. ∴ A2 is true. (There are now 5 true statements and 6 false.)

Complete Solution

A is a Joker.
B is a Wotta-Woppa.
C is a Shilli-Shalla.
D is a Shilli-Shalla.

36. 5 Digits Divided by 2 Digits °

$$
\begin{array}{r}
x\ b\ k\ g \\
g\ t\ )\overline{d\ s\ x\ d\ m} \\
d\ x
\end{array}
$$

	x	b	k	g	(i)
$g\ t\ )$	d	s	x	d	m	(ii)
	d	x				(iii)
	x	x	d			(iv)
	x	t	k			(v)
		p	m			(vi)
		p	g			(vii)
			h			(viii)

(iii) and (vii) are both 2-figure multiples of the divisor, but neither of them is the divisor. ∴ the divisor cannot be more than 33 (33 times 3 = 99). ∴ the first figure of (v), x, must be 1 or 2 (33 times 9 = 297).

But the first figure in (i), x, is not 1 [for (iii) is not the divisor]. ∴ x must be 2. ∴ from (ii), (iii), and (iv), $s = 4$. And in (v), $t = 1$.
∴ $g = 3$ (it cannot be 1 or 2). ∴ in (iii) $d = 6$. And in (vii) $p = 9$. In (i) $b = 0$, and in (v) $k = 7$. And in (vi) and (viii), $m = 8$ and $h = 5$.

Complete Solution

$$
\begin{array}{r}
2\ 0\ 7\ 3 \\
3\ 1\ )\overline{6\ 4\ 2\ 6\ 8} \\
6\ 2 \\
\hline
2\ 2\ 6 \\
2\ 1\ 7 \\
\hline
9\ 8 \\
9\ 3 \\
\hline
5
\end{array}
$$

37. 4 Digits Divided by 2 Digits

$$
\begin{array}{r}
b\ g\ p \\
d\ k\ \overline{)\ k\ x\ m\ k} \\
g\ m \\
\hline
d\ p\ m \\
d\ m\ t \\
\hline
t\ k \\
x\ b \\
\hline
d\ b \\
\hline
\end{array}
$$

(i)
(ii)
(iii)
(iv)
(v)
(vi)
(vii)
(viii)

(The reader is advised to draw a diagram like the one on the right above, and to fill in the digits as they are discovered.)

Since (iii) and (vii) have only 2 figures and are both the divisor times more than 1, the divisor ($d\,k$) must be 33 or less ($33 \times 3 = 99$).

From (vi), (vii), and (viii), $b + b = k$ or $k + 10$. ∴ k must be even.

Since (v) has 3 figures, therefore g in (i) [and ∴ in (iii)] must be at least 4. Therefore k in (ii) must be 6 or 8. ∴ the divisor cannot be more than 28.

And we can now see that g in (iii) cannot be more than 7. $28 \times 7 = 196$. ∴ d in (v) is 1.

Since k is even, therefore b in (vii) is even (all multiples of the divisor are even). If k were 6, then b in (vii) and (viii) would be 3 or 8—but not 3, for b is even, and not 8, for b in (i) cannot be more than 6.

∴ in (vi), (vii), and (viii), k must be 8, and b must be 4.

(iii) is $18 \times 4 = 72$. ∴ $g = 7$, and $m = 2$.

(v) is $18 \times 7 = 126$. ∴ $t = 6$, and in (vii) $x = 5$. And in (iv) $p = 3$.

117

Complete Solution

```
              4 7 3
    1 8 ) 8 5 2 8
          7 2
          ─────
          1 3 2
          1 2 6
          ─────
              6 8
              5 4
              ───
              1 4
              ═══
```

38. Division—but What Has Happened to the Divisor and the Answer?

```
                              (i)
) s  s  t  r  d  m  m  v  v   (ii)      ) – – – – – – – – –
  r  d                        (iii)       – –
 ─────                                   ───
     d  t                     (iv)          – –
     r  d                     (v)           – –
    ─────                                  ───
     v  x  r                  (vi)          – – –
     v  x  v                  (vii)         – – –
    ────────                               ─────
        x  d                  (viii)          – –
        v  y                  (ix)            – –
       ─────                                 ───
        y  m                  (x)             – –
        d  a                  (xi)            – –
       ─────                                 ───
           x  m               (xii)             – –
           v  y               (xiii)            – –
          ─────                                ───
           t  v  v            (xiv)             – – –
           t  t  s            (xv)              – – –
          ────────                            ─────
              s               (xvi)                –
              =                                    =
```

(The reader is advised to draw a figure like the one on the right above, where the digits can be inserted as they are found.)

From (viii), (ix), and (x), $y + y = 10 + d$ (note that 1 had to be borrowed; x is 1 greater than v).

From (x) and (xi), $y - d = 1$. $\therefore 2y - d = 10$

$$y - d = 1$$

Subtract: $\quad y = 9; \quad d = 8$

From (ii), (iii), and (iv), $d + d = 10 + s$ (note that 1 had to be borrowed; s is 1 greater than r). $\therefore$ since $d = 8$, $s = 6$. And since s is 1 greater than r, $r = 5$.

119

From (xiv), (xv), and (xvi), $s + s = 10 + v$ (note that 1 had to be borrowed; v is 1 greater than t). $\therefore$ since $s = 6$, $\therefore$ v = 2, $\therefore$ t = 1.

And since "x is 1 greater than v" (see above), $\therefore x = 3$.

From (xii) $m = 0$, and from (xi) $a = 7$.

(xiii) (29) has no factor; $\therefore$ divisor must be 29. $\therefore$ the answer is: 2 2 8 1 3 1 0 4. (Note the 4 does not appear elsewhere, so we do not know what letter stands for it.)

Complete Solution

```
                2 2 8 1 3 1 0 4
        2 9 ) 6 6 1 5 8 0 0 2 2
              5 8
              ‾‾‾
                8 1
                5 8
                ‾‾‾
                  2 3 5
                  2 3 2
                  ‾‾‾‾‾
                      3 8
                      2 9
                      ‾‾‾
                        9 0
                        8 7
                        ‾‾‾
                          3 0
                          2 9
                          ‾‾‾
                            1 2 2
                            1 1 6
                            ‾‾‾‾‾
                                6
                                =
```

39. I Lose My Specs

$$
\begin{array}{r}
\ \ c\ \ h\ \ b\ \ m \\
i\ \ c\ \overline{)\ b\ \ p\ \ k\ \ g\ \ c\ \ x} \\
m\ \ h\ \ x \\ \hline
s\ \ m\ \ g \\
s\ \ k\ \ p \\ \hline
b\ \ c\ \ c \\
m\ \ b\ \ i \\ \hline
g\ \ x \\
i\ \ c \\ \hline
m\ \ i
\end{array}
$$

  (i)
  (ii)
  (iii)
  (iv)
  (v)
  (vi)
  (vii)
  (viii)
  (ix)
  (x)

The reader is advised to draw a diagram with dashes representing the letters, so that the figures can be filled in as they are found.

We must first try to find out more about the incorrect letter.

Consider (vi), (vii), and (viii). For $(b\ c\ c) - (m\ b\ i)$ to leave a single figure (g), the first c in (vi) would have to be 0. But the figure for c in (i) and the figure for c in the divisor can neither of them be 0. ∴ one of the first 2 figures in (vi) or one of the first 2 figures in (vii) must be incorrect. ∴ all the other figures are correct.

Since (ix) $(i\ c)$ is the divisor, ∴ $m = 1$. ∴ from (ii) and (iii), $b = 2$.

In (iv) and (v), k must be less than m. ∴ since m is 1, k can only be 0. ∴ from (ii), (iii), and (iv), x must be 9. ∴ from (viii), (ix), and (x), $i + c = 9$.

(vii) is the divisor times 2, and it has 3 figures. ∴ the divisor must be 50 or more.

And since (iii) is odd, the divisor must be odd—that is, c is odd. And since $i + c = 9$, the divisor can only be 63 or 81. But c cannot be 1, for m is 1. ∴ the divisor can only be 63. ∴ $i = 6$ and $c = 3$.

(iii) is $63 \times 3 = 189$. ∴ $h = 8$. ∴ (v) is $63 \times 8 = 504$. ∴ $s = 5$ and $p = 4$.

(vii) is $63 \times 2 = 126$, and this is correct.

From (viii), (ix), and (x), $g = 7. \therefore$ (vi) should be $126 + 7 = 133$.

$\therefore$ the first figure in (vi) should be m, not b, and this is the mistake.

Complete Solution

The incorrect letter is the first letter of (vi), b. It should be m.
The correct sum is:

```
              3 8 2 1
      6 3 ) 2 4 0 7 3 9
            1 8 9
            ─────
              5 1 7
              5 0 4
              ─────
                1 3 3
                1 2 6
                ─────
                    7 9
                    6 3
                    ───
                    1 6
                    ═══
```

40. Division: Some Letters for Digits, Some Missing

$$
\begin{array}{r}
- - \; m \; k \\
- - \,\overline{)\, - - - - - \; k} \\
- \; k \; -
\end{array}
$$

$- - \quad m \; k$	(i)
$- - \,)\, - - - - - \; k$	(ii)
$- \; k \; -$	(iii)
$- \; m \; -$	(iv)
$k \; - \; -$	(v)
$- \; -$	(vi)
$- \; m$	(vii)
m	(viii)

From (vi), (vii), and (viii), $m + m = k$, or $k + 10$. ∴ k must be even. (v) is the divisor times m, and has 3 figures; (vii) is the divisor times k and has 2 figures. ∴ m is greater than k. ∴ $m + m = k + 10$. k in (i) cannot be 0; ∴ k is 2, 4, 6, or 8.

∴ (vii) is the divisor times at least 2. ∴ the divisor is less than 50. ∴ k in (v) cannot be more than 4 ($49 \times 9 = 441$). If k were 4, then, since m is greater than k, m would be 7 ($7 + 7 = 14$). But since (vii) is the divisor times 2 or 4, it must be even. ∴ m cannot be 7, and k cannot be 4. ∴ $k = 2$ and $m = 6$.

(v) $(2 - -)$ is the divisor times 6. ∴ the divisor must start with 3 or 4 (not 2, for $30 \times 6 = 180$). And since (vii) $(- 6)$ is the divisor times 2, ∴ the divisor must end with 3 or 8 ($2 \times 3 = 6$; $2 \times 8 = 16$). If the divisor were 33, then (v) would be $33 \times 6 = 198$. But (v) starts with 2. ∴ (v) is not 33.

If the divisor were 38, then (v) would be $38 \times 6 = 228$. But it would not then be possible for the second digit of (iv) to be 6. ∴ (iv) is not 38.

If the divisor were 48, then (v) would be 288. But (v) would then be more than (iv), which is not possible. ∴ the divisor can only be 43.

∴ (vii) is $43 \times 2 = 86$; (v) is $43 \times 6 = 258$.

And since the second figure of (iii) is 2, (iii) can only be 129 (43×3).

Add up from the bottom and we get:

Complete Solution

```
              3 0 6 2
    4 3 ) 1 3 1 6 7 2
          1 2 9
          ─────
              2 6 7
              2 5 8
              ─────
                  9 2
                  8 6
                  ───
                      6
                      ═══
```

41. Addition (2 Numbers)

B	H	C	X	D	B	F	(i)
D	M	A	C	G	B	F	(ii)

F	B	B	G	B	M	G	B	(iii)

The most that can be carried when 2 digits are added together is 1. ∴ F = 1. ∴ from last digits of (i), (ii), and (iii), B = 2. And since (iii) starts 12, and first figure of (i) is 2, ∴ first figure of (ii) must be 9. ∴ D = 9 (and there must have been 1 to carry from H + M).

From last digits but one of (i), (ii), and (iii), G = 2 + 2 = 4. From fifth digits of (i) and (ii), and from sixth digit of (iii), M = 9 + 4 − 10 = 3. From second digits of (i) and (ii) and third digit of (iii), H + 3 + (perhaps) 1 = 2. We know that H is not 9, for D is 9; ∴ H = 8 (and there is 1 to carry).

From last digits but three of (i), (ii), and (iii), X + C + 1 = 12; ∴ X + C = 11.

Neither X nor C can be 1, 2, 3, 4, 8, or 9 (for F = 1, B = 2, M = 3, G = 4, H = 8, and D = 9). ∴ X and C must be 5 and 6 (but we cannot tell yet which is which).

From third digits of (i) and (ii) and fourth digit of (iii), C + A + 1 = 14; ∴ C + A = 13. ∴ C and A must be 6 and 7.

∴ C = 6, X = 5, and A = 7.

Complete Solution

	2	8	6	5	9	2	1
	9	3	7	6	4	2	1

1	2	2	4	2	3	4	2

42. Addition (3 Numbers)

```
E  R  K  K  T
E  S  E  D  T
E  K  K  T  T
─────────────
T  T  R  V  T
```

Consider the last line down. T can only be 0 or 5 $(0 + 0 + 0 = 0$; and $5 + 5 + 5 = 15)$. But not 0 (see first line down). $\therefore$ T = 5. $\therefore$ in first line down E = 1, and there are 2 to carry from second line down. $\therefore$ second line down comes to 25 (with 0, 1, or 2 to be carried from third line down).

The most that second line down can be is $9 + 8 + 7$ (that is, 24), so there must be at least 1 to carry from third line down.

In third line down, E = 1, K is 9, 8, 7, or 6; and R is 9, 8, 7, or 6. So there must be 1 to carry, but there cannot be 2 (we would then have at least 9) $+ 1 + 9 +$ not more than 2 to carry, which could not be more than 21; but if there is 2 to carry from third line down, it would have to add up to at least 26.

$\therefore$ there is only 1 to carry from third line down; $\therefore$ R, S, and K are 9, 8, and 7, but we do not yet know which is which.

Suppose K were 9, then the third line down would be $9 + 1 + 9 = 19$. And R would have to be 9, or if there is something to carry from fourth line, R would be 0 or 1, and we know that it is not. $\therefore$ K is not 9.

Suppose K were 7, then third line down would be $7 + 1 + 7 = 15$, or if there is 1 or 2 to carry, 16 or 17. But R cannot be 5 or 6, and if K were 7, R cannot be 7 too. $\therefore$ K = 8. And third line down is $8 + 1 + 8 = 17$ (with perhaps something to carry). R, at end of third line down, is 7 or 9. Fourth line down is $8 + D + 5$, so we know that there is at least 1 to carry. $\therefore$ R is not 7. And it cannot be 8 for K = 8. $\therefore$ R = 9. $\therefore$ S = 7. And there are 2 to carry from fourth line down. $\therefore$ D must be 6 (it cannot be more) and V = 0 (8 $+ 6 + 5 + 1 = 20)$.

```
  1 9 8 8 5
  1 7 1 6 5
  1 8 8 5 5
  ─────────
  5 5 9 0 5
  ═════════
```

43. Addition: Uncle's Error

	B	L	A	L	E	D	Y
	B	Y	S	X	P	S	Y
ix	B	L	A	X	E	P	Y
	Y	Y	R	R	S	G	G	B

	i	ii	iii	iv	v	vi	vii	viii

Look first for the incorrect letter.

There are 11 letters here (A, B, D, E, G, L, P, R, S, X, Y). But there are only 10 digits (0 to 9).

∴ 1 letter should not be there. And since only 1 letter is wrong "on one of the occasions on which it appears," it must be a letter that only appears once.

But the only letter that only appears once is D [in (vii)]. ∴ D is the incorrect letter, and all other letters are correct.

Y in (i) must be 1 or 2. Suppose it is 2, then B in (viii) would be 6. ∴ (ii) would be (6 + 6 + 6) + (at most) 2 carried from (iii)—that is, not more than 20. But if Y were 2, (ix) should start 22. ∴ our assumption is wrong, ∴ Y = 1. ∴ B in (viii) is 3. ∴ 2 must be carried from (iii) to (ii) (3 + 3 + 3 + 2 = 11). ∴ in (iii), since Y = 1, L must be 9 and R must be 0. [9 + 1 + 9 + 1 (carried) = 20.] And there is 1 to carry from (iv) to (iii).

Consider (iv). A + S + A + (perhaps) 1 or 2 carried = 10. Remembering that we know which letters stand for 0, 1, and 3, (iv) might be 4 + 2 + 4 = 10. But there would be at least 1 carried from (v) (at least 5 + 5 + 6); ∴ A cannot be 4, and must be 2, and S must be 4 or 5.

Suppose S in (iv) were 5. There would then only be 1 carried from (v). (v) would then be 9 + X + X + (perhaps) 1 or 2 carried, and this would have to be 15. But this is not possible, for we know that X must be at least 4. ∴ S cannot be 5. ∴ S = 4. ∴ 2 is carried from (v) to (iv).

If X in (v) were 8, we would have 9 + 8 + 8 = 25; and this is too much. ∴ X must be 7 [9 + 7 + 7 = 23, and 1 is carried from (vi)].

E, G, and P must now be 5, 6, and 8, but we do not know which is which.

If E were 8 and P were 5 or 6, 2 would be carried from (vi). If E were 6 and P were 8, 2 would be carried from (vi). If E were 5 and P were 8, G would be 8 [apart from anything that might be carried from (vii)]. But G ought to be 6. ∴ G must be 8.

If E were 5 and P were 6, we would have (5 + 6 + 5), and 2 would have to be carried from (vii) to make 18. But (vii) would then be (D + 4 + 6) = 28, and D would have to be more than 10 to make this possible. ∴ the only possibility is for E to be 6 and P to be 5, and for there to be 1 to carry from (vii) (6 + 5 + 6 + 1 = 18). (vii) is now D + 4 + 5 = 18; ∴ D must be 9 (L).

Complete Solution

D should be L (9)

```
  3 9 2 9 6 9 1
  3 1 4 7 5 4 1
  3 9 2 7 6 5 1

1 1 0 0 4 8 8 3
```

44. Multiplication

$$
\begin{array}{ccccccc}
E & B & P & N & Y & E & \text{(i)} \\
  &   &   &   &   & E & \text{(ii)} \\
\hline
Y & N & H & Y & A & X & \text{(iii)} \\
\hline
\end{array}
$$

E in (ii) can clearly not be 0 or 1. If E were 4, then since E is the first figure in (i), and since 4 times 4 is 16, there would be another figure in (iii). ∴ E must be 2 or 3. If E were 3, then X in (iii) would be 9. But since the first figure in (iii) is not X, but Y, there would have been something to carry from the next line. But this would mean that Y would have to be 10 or more, which is not possible. ∴ E can only be 2. ∴ X is 4.

Since we are multiplying by 2, there can never be more than 1 to carry. ∴ Y [the first letter in (iii)] must be 5. And since there is not 1 to carry from 2 times 2, A must be 0.

2 times N + 1 = 5 or 15. But not 5, for N would then be (but E is 2). ∴ N = 7 [(2 × 7) + 1 = 15].

Since N is 7, there must have been 1 to carry from the third line down to the second line down, and since we know that there is 1 to carry to the first line down, B must be 8 [(2 × 8) + 1 = 17]. And since 1, 3, 6, and 9 are the only digits left, it is easy to see that P must be 6, and H must be 3 [(2 × 6) + 1 = 13].

Complete Solution

$$
\begin{array}{ccccccc}
2 & 8 & 6 & 7 & 5 & 2 \\
  &   &   &   &   & 2 \\
\hline
5 & 7 & 3 & 5 & 0 & 4 \\
\hline
\end{array}
$$

45. Cross-Number Puzzle (3 by 3)

Consider 5 across and 3 down. 5 across can only be 19, 38, 57, 76, or 95. ∴ 3 down must be 765, 876, or 987. But 4 across is odd; ∴ 3 down can only be 876. ∴ 5 across is 76. From 1 across and 4 across, both digits of 1 down must be even; ∴ 1 down can only be 64.

2 down is a perfect square when reversed; and when reversed it is 7 – – and can only be the square of 27 (729) or 28 (784). But from 1 across the first digit of 2 down must be even. ∴ 2 down is 487.

Complete Solution

^{1}6	^{2}4	^{3}8
^{4}4	8	7
■	^{5}7	6

46. Cross-Number Puzzle, with One Clue Wrong (5 by 5)

(i) We must first try to find the incorrect clue. The last digit of 8 across must be 3 or 1. 7 down is a perfect square, but there is no 3-figure perfect square whose second digit is 1 or 3. ∴ either 8 across or 7 down must be the incorrect clue. ∴ all the other clues are correct.

(ii) 5 down must be even; ∴ 6 across starts with an even number. But the only 3-figure cube that starts with an even number is the cube of 6 (216). The only 2-figure multiples of 8 ending in 2 are 32 and 72. ∴ the first figure of 5 across is 3 or 7, and the last figure is also 3 or 7. 4 down is a multiple of 25; ∴ the second digit cannot be 3, and is therefore 7; ∴ the first figure of 5 across must also be 7; and the third figure of 4 down is 5. ∴ the first figure of 7 across is 9; ("the square of an even number" can only be 16).

(iii) The last digit of 1 across must be 4 or more. 9 across is a prime factor of 4 down; ∴ it cannot be a multiple of 5 or 25; ∴ 4 down must be 25 × a prime number. The possibilities are 475 (25 × 19), 575 (25 × 23), and 775 (25 × 31). But 8 down is even; ∴ 9 across is 23, 8 down is 92, and 4 down is 575.

(iv) The first digit of 1 across must be 1 or 2; but not 1, for 1 is the third digit of 1 down; ∴ 2. ∴ 1 across is 2345.

(v) 2 down can only be 3969. ∴ 8 across must be the incorrect clue. ∴ 7 down is correct and must be 961. ∴ 10 across is 19.

(vi) The second figure of 1 down (and therefore the second figure of 5 across) must be 4 or 5. But not 4 (see 3 down and 5 across). ∴ it is 5, and 3 down is 45, and the fourth figure of 1 down is 4.

8 across is the incorrect clue.

	¹2	²3	³4	⁴5
⁵7	5	9	5	7
⁶2	1	6	⁷9	5
⁸9	4	9	6	
⁹2	3		¹⁰1	9

47. "Our Factory Started with Just a Sweeper-Upper"

Sweeper-Upper = SU; Door-Opener = DO; Bottle-Washer = BW; Welfare Officer = WO; Worker = W.

We know that there is: "An officer of welfare, and Ernie was his name." We also know that: "Alf has not the Worker's or the Bottle-Washer lot." Suppose that D's statement "I am the Worker" is true and that his statement that "the SU is C" is false. Then we have:

	SU	DO	BW	WO	W
A			X	X	X
B				X	X
C	X			X	X
D	X	X	X	X	✔
E	X	X	X	✔	X

And it would not be true that "you can find just who does what."

Let us suppose that D's other statement is true, so that "the SU is C," and "I am the W" is false. We now have:

	SU	DO	BW	WO	W
A	X		X	X	X
B	X			X	
C	✔	X	X	X	X
D	X			X	X
E	X	X	X		X

∴ B must be W (no one else can be). A is DO. ∴ D is BW and E is WO.

134

Complete Solution

Alf is Door-Opener.
Bert is Worker.
Charlie is Sweeper-Upper.
Duggie is Bottle-Washer.
Ernie is Welfare Officer.

48. French and Mathematics at the Factory

Since B's French was above his math, ∴ B was not first at math, and not fourth at French. Since C's math was below his French, C is not first at math, and not fourth in French. A's place was even at both, and D's was odd at both. And B was not first at either. ∴ the possibilities are:

	French				Math			
1		C	D		1			D
2	A	B	C		2	A	B	C
3		B	C	D	3		B	C	D
4	A				4	A	B	C

∴ A was fourth at French, and D was first at math. Since D was first at math, D was not first at French.

∴ C was first at French and B was second at French (no one else can be). ∴ D was third at French. A cannot be fourth at math (for A was fourth at French). ∴ A was second at math.

C was first at French and third or fourth at math, and B was second at French and third or fourth at math. But B's French place was as much above his math place as C's French place was above his math place. ∴ C must have been third at math, and B was fourth.

Complete Solution

FRENCH	1. Charlie
	2. Bert
	3. Duggie
	4. Alf

MATHEMATICS	1. Duggie
	2. Alf
	3. Charlie
	4. Bert

49. Rules

A diagram will help. (Work in units of 10 pence; call this 1p. ∴ wages are between 290p and 190p inclusive.)

	DS	DO	BW	W	Wages
A	X				
B		X	X	X	$\left(\dfrac{5}{4}(BW - 20)\,p\right)$
C	X	X			200p or 225p
D	X				
Wages		216p or 243p		246p or 273p	

(i) From (1), DO gets $\dfrac{90}{100} \times \dfrac{120}{100} \times C = \dfrac{9}{10} \times \dfrac{6}{5} \times C = \dfrac{27}{25}$ $\times$ C. ∴ DO is not C. And $\dfrac{DO}{C} = \dfrac{27}{25}$ etc. $= \dfrac{216}{200} = \dfrac{243}{225} = \dfrac{270}{250}$.

(ii) From (2), B gets $\dfrac{125}{100}(BW - 20)p = \dfrac{5}{4}(BW - 20)p$.

Suppose B's wages = BW's wages (call this x); then $x = \dfrac{5}{4}(x - 20)$.

∴ $4x = 5x - 100$. ∴ $x = 100$. But x cannot be 100p, for wages are between 290p and 190p. ∴ B is not BW.

(iii) If DO gets 270p, then W gets 300p, which is impossible [see (3)]. ∴ DO gets 216p or 243p; and C gets 200p or 225 p.

(iv) B's wages are m(5), $\left[\dfrac{5}{4}(BW - 20)p\right]$. ∴ B is not DO

(wages 216p or 243p). W gets 30p more than DO; ∴ W gets 246p or 273p. But B's wages are m(5); ∴ W is not B. ∴ by elimination B is DS. (Information so far has been inserted in diagram.)

(v) C gets 200p or 225 p. W gets 246p or 273p. ∴ C is not W. ∴ by elimination C is BW.

137

(vi) B's wages are $\left[\dfrac{5}{4}(BW - 20)p\right]$. ∴ BW's wages must be m(2). ∴ BW's (C's) wages are 200p, not 225p. ∴ DO's wages are 216p, W's wages are 246p, and B's wages are 225p.

(vii) And from (4), A gets 216p and is DO. And D gets 246p and is W.

Complete Solution

Alf is Door-Opener; his wages are £21.60.
Bert is Door-Shutter; his wages are £22.50.
Charlie is Bottle-Washer; his wages are £20.00.
Duggie is Worker; his wages are £24.60.

50. 3 Teams

A, B, and C all played at least one game, for they had goals for or against. But none of them can have played more than 2. ∴ t, x, and r must be 0, 1, and 2, and since t and x must be 1 and 2 or 2 and 1, r must be 0.

If t were 2 and x were 1, the total of matches played would be $(2 + 1 + 2) = 5$. But the total must be even, for each must appear twice. ∴ $t = 1$ and $x = 2$.

d (B's points) cannot be 0, 1, or 2; ∴ it must be 3 or 4. (No side can get more than 4 points.)

But from A's and B's goals, neither of them drew their match. ∴ d must be 4. And since C lost their match vs. B, p can only be 3. And C vs. B was 3–4. And A vs. B was 2–3.

∴ n is 7 $(3 + 4)$ and g is 5 $(2 + 3)$.

Complete Solution

A vs. B	2–3
B vs. C	4–3

51. 4 Teams

k and x (A's and C's played) and s (C's wins) and t (B's draws) cannot be more than 3 (no teams can play more than 3 matches). ∴ among them they must be 0, 1, 2, and 3. ∴ g (C's points) must be 4, 5, or 6 (no teams can get more than 6 points). ∴ C must have won at least 1; ∴ s must be 1 or 2. k and x cannot be 0; ∴ t (B's draws) must be 0.

∴ A's goals for are less than A's goals against (since A got no points).

∴ k is less than x (A's goals for and against). And since x must be more than s (C's wins); ∴ x can only be 3.

If k (A's played) were 2, then t (A's points) could not be 0, for with 2 goals for and 3 against, A would have got at least 1 point from 2 matches. ∴ k must be 1; ∴ $s = 2$. ∴ A vs. C was 1–3.

D must have played 1 or 2 games (not 3, for only A played C). But if they had played 2 and drawn 1, their goals for could not be the same as their goals against. ∴ D only played C, and the score was 1–1.

∴ B can only have played 1 match vs. C. C won 2 and drew 1; ∴ they got 5 points. ∴ $g = 5$. ∴ B lost their match vs. C; ∴ their goals against must be more than their goals for.

y (B's goals for) must be at least 4 (t, k, s, and x are 0, 1, 2, and 3). ∴ their goals against must be at least 5. And in that case h (C's goals for) would be $(3 + 5 + 1) = 9$. ∴ since h cannot be more than 9, B's goals against can only be 5. ∴ B vs. C was 4–5. ∴ $h = 9$.

Complete Solution

A vs. C	1–3
B vs. C	4–5
C vs. D	1–1

52. Soccer and Addition

Consider (i). y, m, p, and t must be 0, 1, 2, and 3, but we do not yet know which is which.

∴ in (ii) x can only be 4; ∴ h is 8. ∴ f (B's points) cannot be 0, 1, 2, 3, or 4. ∴ f must be 5 or 6. ∴ m (B's wins) must be 2 or 3. But not 3, for y must be greater than m.

∴ $y = 3$ and $m = 2$. ∴ since B only won 2, f must be 5.

∴ p (B's lost) is 0. ∴ t (C's draws) is 1. D had 0 (p) goals for and 1 (t) goals against, and got no points. ∴ D only played 1 match (if they had played more with the same number of goals, it could only have been 0–0, and they would have got points). ∴ D only played B.

∴ C played 1 or 2. If C played 2 and drew only 1, it would not have been possible for their goals for to be the same as their goals against. ∴ C only played B.

∴ A can only have played B (there is no one else for them to play). We know that B vs. C is 2–2 and B vs. D is 1–0. And we know that A vs. B is 3 (y) vs. g.

$g + 2 + 1$ (A's, C's, and D's goals against) = k (B's goals for). ∴ $k - g = 3$. And since k and g cannot be 0, 1, 2, 3, 4, 5, or 8, they can only be 9 and 6. ∴ $k = 9$, and $g = 6$. ∴ A vs. B is 3–6.

Complete Solution

(i) A vs. B   3–6
    B vs. C   2–2
    B vs. D   1–0

(ii)   4
  + 4
  ―――
    8
   ═══